Mapping Change

and

Innovation

Gerald G. Smale

Director of Development, National Institute for Social Work
Visiting Professor Goldsmiths College, University of London

London : HMSO

...stitute for Social Work
...vistock Place
London WC1H 9SN
Tel: 0171 387 9681

© **1996 Gerald G. Smale**

ISBN 011 702004 4

Published by HMSO and available from:

HMSO Publications Centre
(Mail, fax and telephone orders only)
PO Box 276, London SW8 5DT
Telephone orders 0171 873 9090
General enquiries 0171 873 0011
(queing system in operation for both numbers)
Fax orders 0171 873 8200

HMSO Bookshops
49 High Holborn, London WC1V 6HB
(counter service only)
0171 873 0011 Fax 0171 831 1326
68–69 Bull Street, Birmingham B4 6AD
0121 236 9696 Fax 0121 236 9699
33 Wine Street, Bristol BS1 2BQ
0117 9264306 Fax 0117 9294515
9–21 Princess Street, Manchester M60 8AS
0161 834 7201 Fax 0161 833 0634
16 Arthur Street, Belfast BT1 4GD
01232 238451 Fax 01232 235401
71 Lothian Road, Edinburgh EH3 9AZ
0131 228 4181 Fax 0131 229 2734
The HMSO Oriel Bookshop
The Friary, Cardiff CF1 4AA
01222 395548 Fax 01222 384347

HMSO's Accredited Agents
(see Yellow Pages)

and through good booksellers

Printed in the UK for HMSO Dd 301310 C20 4/96

In memory of

Tim Smale

July 27th 1978 – July 23rd 1995

whose enthusiasm for change inspired us all.

Acknowledgments

In 1983 a grant from the Joseph Rowntree Foundation enabled us to set up the Practice And Development Exchange, PADE at the National Institute for Social Work, NISW. The aim of the Exchange was to work with innovatory managers, practitioners and researchers to develop better models of practice and management based on the best available evidence. This started us on the road to finding better ways of supporting innovation and managing change. Since then I have had the privilege of working with many who led change in their organisations and have been leaders in their fields. I would like to thank them all, particularly the many innovators of the PADE networks.

This book gives a brief description of the Managing Change Through Innovation, MCTI approach, and presents the questions that need to be addressed to build up plans for managing change in local circumstances. A full discussion of the approach takes place in the companion volume of that name. The third book in the set, Chance Favours the Prepared Mind describes the development of services using the approach and relating it to a discussion of leadership and team building. All are published by HMSO.

These books grew out of the work of PADE and the Management of Change and Innovations Programme. My thanks go to all the members of the NISW; Kings Fund Consultancy Development Programme; staff from all levels of management in Warwickshire, Wigan, Westminster and Newcastle Social Services departments and Cambridgeshire Probation Service; and the students who participated in MCTI workshops as part of their management and advanced practice courses at the Universities of Southampton, Sussex, Sterling and Dundee. The members of the Scottish Network and workshops have been a constant source of stimulation and support throughout.

It will be clear from the text that I owe a particular debt to the work of Everrett Rogers, and Barbara Stocking who drew attention to research on the diffusion of innovations, Watzlawick and his colleges from Palo Alto, Rosabeth Moss - Kanter and Van de Ven and Angle.

I would also like to thank the Colleagues from the USA who have engaged with us and enriched our ideas including those who participated through the Federally Funded Transfer of Technology Project on Community Based Practice in Cedar Rapids and at the University of Iowa; participants at the Wingspread Conference on Community Based Practice funded by the Johnson Foundation; the Transferring Human Services Technology to Pennsylvania Rural Counties project funded by the Center for Rural Pennsylvania; the 1994 Obermann Seminar at the University of Iowa; and the National Association of Social Workers conference on Effective Programme Replication and Adaption in Washington D.C.

I have received exceptional support from the Management of Change and Innovations Advisory Group: Fabian Best, David Crosbie, Maneck Dalal, Chris Gostick, David Mason, Joyce Moseley, Stephen Osborne, John Starzewski and especially Robert Maxwell of the Kings fund who chaired the group and its parental predecessor for the Practice Development Exchange.

Several colleagues at NISW and from other organisations in the UK and USA have been particularly helpful including: Paul Adams, John Brown, Nan Carle, Colin Cheesman, Bob Cohen, Mike Cooper, Giles Darvill, Gayle Foster, Sheila Gallagher, Raymond Green, John Griffiths, David Harrison, Barbara Hearn, Trish Kearney, Wendy Macfarlane, Margo MacLellan, Wendy Mertons, Khristy Nelson, Daphne Statham, Graham Tuson, Mike Wardel, Roger Winter and Stan Witkin. Christine Crosbie gave excellent editorial assisstance when help was much needed. Jeanette Eno and Lynette Domoney provided crucial help by scaling the mountain of literature that exists on innovation and change and coming back with manageable information and useful insights.

Our funders made this programme possible and had the vision to recognise that the way that change was tackled in the field is not always the best way for it to be managed. Although their support was invaluable they can not be held responsible for the conclusions that we have arrived at nor are the views expressed those of either the Department of Health Social Services Inspectorate of the Social Work Inspectorate of the Scottish Office. We received particular encouragement from Don Brand, David Crosbie, Linda Hunt and Alex Skinner.

Finally the project owes more than the usual debt to those who anchor the unit when we are on the road as well as providing an essential contribution to the final product: Lynette Bolitho, Nancy Dunlop, Dionne Mortley, Nnennaya Onyckwere.

Cartoons by Michelle Cirkel.

The Author

Gerry Smale trained in production management with the Ford Motor Company before joining the Probation Service. He has been director of a social work qualifying course for mature entrants at Sussex University, post graduate management development programmes and founding director of the National Institute for Social Works Practice and Development Exchange, PADE. He has carried out staff and management development programmes and consultancies throughout the UK and in the USA. Recent work includes, the transfer of technology on community based practice to the USA and directing the Management of Innovations and Change programme. He is currently working on the Management and Development of Practice Expertise Programme supported by the DoH and a consortium of Social Services Departments. Recent publications include Empowerment, Assessment, Care Management and the Skilled Worker, and Negotiating Care in the Community both published by HMSO.

Contents

Introduction

The purpose of this book

This book attempts to help those managing change, particularly those introducing and developing new forms of practice and service delivery. It is not about introducing optional extras to mainstream services. It is about implementing new policy. It is about changing practice for the better, innovating to meet new problems or to apply better solutions to long standing ones. Many innovations are born of necessity, not the product of the luxury of free time. They are often invented and adopted in response to crisis, either an acute lack of staff or money, the persistence of hitherto insoluble problems, or a new problem making new demands on existing, stretched resources. This book presents the central ideas that we have found useful in working with managers introducing new approaches to practice and new forms of service delivery.

The approach presented here has been tried and tested with managers and practitioners from both the social services and the health services working in a variety of settings including social service departments, national and local Voluntary Organisations and health care trusts. Senior, middle and first line managers, professional practitioners and people in service user organisations have been involved, both individually and as part of whole directorates, departmental and inter-agency teams.

The ideas and the research which underpins this approach, are not limited to the 'human services'. *The approach can be applied to introducing innovations into any social organisation.*

3

This book is based on the research and practice of the Managing Change and Innovation Programme of the National Institute for Social Work. Working with innovatory managers and practitioners for over a decade we came to a series of conclusions about:

- the nature of change;
- the processes involved in developing new approaches to practice.

We noticed that many innovations, even the most effective ones, failed repeatedly to become mainstream practice, even when national and local policies supported them. By contrast, other innovations seemed to be readily adopted, even if there was no evidence that they were more effective than the previous status quo. Even major reorganisations often make little difference to practice: the way people behave when they are carrying out their tasks.

Indeed it seems that many of the ways in which new forms of practice are developed and introduced actually inoculate the organisation against adoption rather than leading to widespread implementation of new forms of work.

We also found that a single common problem persisted no matter what area of practice and management we were involved in: how do you change anything in an organisation and particularly the way people in it relate to the public and to other professionals?

The way that change is managed, and specifically the way that new approaches to practice and service delivery are introduced, is crucial. Yet, few managers have explicit approaches to introducing innovations and many do not recognise the need for planned approaches to managing change. To be more precise, many managers have *implicit* ways in which they set about introducing change. Sometimes these rest on the ways in which the organisation typically sets about responding to change, for example, reorganisations to implement new social policies coupled with 'retraining' or replacement of staff. Sometimes they rest on 'instinct' and 'political acumen'. Increasingly, they are influenced by the theories of current management gurus. Often they act on a mixture of all three, focusing exclusively on how the new practice or service should operate, at the expense of attention to the detailed process of getting there.

It is also clear that many of the approaches used do not work for all kinds of change, and worse, that some actually precipitate consequences that are the opposite to the intentions of the changes that are espoused. Common examples include 'decentralisations' that decrease local autonomy, 'needs-led' assessment procedures in community care that are more explicitly service driven than the service-led practice they replaced and 'tailor made' services and products that quickly become a new range of 'off the peg' options.

About this approach

'I wish that they would come and look at what we are doing now and find out why we do it this way before they sweep it all away again with the next round of change'.

These heart felt words come from the representative of a group of managers and practitioners confronted with their department's latest round of 'major changes'. They had embraced the last set of 'reforms' and put considerable energy and commitment into changing their practice and services. Now a new agenda had been drawn up and another reorganisation proposed to introduce the latest policy on practice and service delivery. The plans for this round of reforms were drawn up on 'clean sheets of paper' elsewhere in the organisation. It was assumed that all would have to change to work to new procedures and that staff would be regrouped into new teams designed to implement revised policy. The policy was then communicated to staff through new job descriptions, procedures and practice guidelines accompanied by as much training as very limited resources allow.

By contrast to such a strategy, the approach described in this book invites change managers to start by identifying *'who sees what as a problem'*, to be clear about *'what needs to change'*, and to address the vital question: *'what should stay the same?'*.

No management theory or practice can guarantee fixed outcomes, no one person, or group of people, can have that much control over the complex processes involved or the ever-changing context within which they work. But by making sure that the way you are managing change is consistent with the innovations that you are introducing you may avoid the worst unintended consequences that are so often the result of our best intentions to reform practice.

Managers and practitioners using the approach described in this book have found that it helped them to identify 'who they need to do what with'. It enables them to map their way through complex terrain and overcome obstacles as they try to change practice. For the experienced innovator the approach crystallises and 'legitimises' what they have done and adds to their repertoires as change agents.

Some managers and practitioners attempting to develop new approaches get stuck along the way. Conventional ideas about managing change enable them to recognise other people's 'resistance', without always suggesting how this might be 'overcome'.

> *'We know exactly what we should be doing and everybody says that they agree that we should be working in that way but somehow we are always blocked and things stay much the same.'*

The approach described here has helped such managers understand why they are experiencing difficulties and how to find a path through them. While not denying that many people **appear** to be 'resistant to change', this approach invites change managers to go beyond this interpretation of people's behaviour by using the 'innovation trinity' (described below).

Other managers and staff feel that they are on the receiving end of change, that policy makers and change managers are ignoring them in the difficult processes of transition, yet at the end of the day, expect them to practice the new order. Even with the best intentions it is easy to do violence to some people and their work when introducing change. The approach described here of 'managing change **through** innovations' in management has helped change managers to recognise more of the consequences of their actions.

People using this approach have described it as 'street-wise', perhaps because it rests on the experience of those who have been most successful in changing things. It has also been described as 'subversive'. Planning changes in the status quo often 'feels' subversive. This is an important feature of any innovation, not just this approach. Innovation involves departing from the status quo, what the geneticist Conrad Waddington called: *'the conventional wisdom of the dominant group' or 'COWDUNG' for short.* Whether this is seen as 'subversion', or some other kind of deviance, depends upon who is taking the initiative, and who is seen as maintaining the status quo. It helps 'change managers' to recognise that these dynamics are at play within the relationships they work in. They might find it helpful to consider the following:

If innovation is deviance from the status quo then:

'Delinquency' is deviance with authority organised against you.

'Leadership' is deviance with authority.

How to use this book

The boxed sections of this book are intended to be used as a workbook which can be completed by readers to produce their own maps and plans for managing change in their own situations. The surrounding text presents the major issues that need to be addressed to introduce innovations: to change front line practice and management. It explains the basis of the approach and indicates some of the research and practice on which it is based. For a full explanation of the approach readers will need to consult the companion volume *Managing Change Through Innovation* also published by HMSO (Smale, 1996). A detailed description of the management of major changes in social services practice using the approach can be found in the third publication in this set: *Chance Favours the Prepared Mind* (Brown and Wardle, 1996: HMSO).

Our approach is not a model in the sense that it is a step by step guide or blueprint that can be followed in order to reach a predetermined destination. It is an approach which provides a set of related ideas drawn from a wide body of experience, research and management literature. It is essentially flexible - designed to be adapted to meet the needs of a variety of situations.

In Chapter 1 we define the terms 'change' and 'innovation' and consider the ways they will be used in this book.

In Chapter 2 we clear the ground for using our approach by describing the *simple linear model* - the most common method which managers currently use to introduce change and innovation - and analyse its major shortcomings.

In Chapter 3 we look at a range of implicit or explicit theories people use to describe how the process of change works which we have called *'the fallacies'*.

In Chapter 4 we consider the fundamental problem-solving issues which underpin introducing innovations and managing change: who sees what as a problem and who believes certain innovations will solve these problems.

The rest of the book takes the reader through a suggested process for introducing innovation which, for the purposes of clarity, we have divided into four levels as follows:

Level 1: The first stage concerns the crucial analysis of:
- *what changes - what stays the same;*

and introduces the process of:
- *mapping innovation and change* (Chapter 5).

Level 2: *The innovation trinity* is the core of the approach with three parts as follows:

I *Mapping the people to identify all the key players* (Chapter 6)

II *Analysing the innovation to plan action* (Chapter 7)

III *Understanding the context to use it to your advantage* (Chapter 8).

Level 3: Focuses on the:
- *Negotiations, staff and organisation development* (Chapter 9) that need to be undertaken.

Level 4: *Feedback, consequences and changing change management:*
(Chapter 10) looks at the need to identify the impact of intervention on all dimensions of the situation in order to manage the continuous process of change.

To assist in the process we use three different forms of presentation:

Fundamental points are highlighted drawing attention to the main issues and arguments being discussed

MAPPING BOXES

This book provides a guide to map making. At each critical phase in the process, you are invited to draw a MAP of the significant people on the path of the changes you are managing. These changing maps will be worked on from different perspectives as you develop and carry out your planned change. Your map should identify all of the people you will need to communicate with to answer the Key Questions.

KEY QUESTION BOXES

Boxed questions occur at key points throughout the text. Addressing these questions will enable you to plan your management of change and the way that you can introduce innovations in your own situation.
The mapping boxes and these questions constitute a workbook for planning and managing the complex processes of change and innovation.

Answering these questions will enable you to develop maps of your situation and a route or plan of the action required to achieve change.

At this stage you may find it helpful to identify an innovation that you are working on now and the changes that you are having to manage.

CHAPTER ONE

Defining Change and Innovation

Originally, we made a clear distinction between 'the management of innovations' and 'the management of change'. 'Managing innovations' is used here to refer to the introduction of specific new practices, methods of work or pieces of technology. 'Managing change' is a wider concept applied to many kinds of change including: restructuring organisations, changes in context within which agencies function, changes in the nature of the social problems that they confront, changes in the goals or mission of the enterprise, or significant changes in personnel. The distinction between 'managing change' and 'managing innovation' continues to be central to our approach, but we no longer see them as separate enterprises: *'Managing change' involves 'managing a series of innovations'*.

Common perceptions of change and innovation

Many of the managers whom we have worked with make a distinction between 'innovation' and 'change'. 'Innovation' is typically seen as 'good'. Most say that they want to run organisations that encourage staff to innovate, to be constantly developing better ways of tackling problems and improving service delivery. But innovation is also seen as a luxury that can be entered into at times of relative calm, and dropped when under pressure. Change on the other hand is seen as inevitable and omnipresent. This has been especially true during recent times when managers and staff in the 'human services' have been preoccupied with introducing wide ranging changes through the National Health Service and Community Care Act and the Children Act. This perception of change is the same in industry and commerce. Here changing markets and technology are seen as constantly driving accelerating change in products, forms of service delivery and the nature of organisations themselves.

The kind of distinctions made by many managers can be illustrated by the following incident. At the beginning of the NISW project on the Management of Innovations, a social services director was asked if he thought that managers from his department would participate in the project. He said:

'We would really like to, but we are facing up to all the National Health and Community Care reforms and implementing the Children Act. New information technology is about to be introduced, radically affecting working practices, and local government reorganisations are on the horizon. With all this going on there is no chance that staff will have time to innovate'.

Slightly different versions of this response have been very common. When we tell this story many smile at the paradox: 'we are too busy changing to look at how we are managing innovation and change'. But many know exactly how this director felt and identify with him and his dilemma.

Further discussion reveals that implicit in responses such as this director's is a distinction between 'innovation' - an optional addition to what has to be done, the invention of new ways of working - and 'change'. Change in this context refers to the obligatory implementation of policy changes and responses to new or different conditions for the agency to work in. Typically, we also find that a way of managing these changes is contained within the statements. Very often the implied approach is led by restructuring parts, or all, of the organisation, combined with redrafting agency procedures and job descriptions and 'staff training'. As we will see, these approaches to managing change often prove to have little or no effect at best and, at worst, to be counter-productive (see Chapters 2 and 3).

Unpacking these uses of the terms we see that 'innovation' is perceived as something that you have some control over while 'change' happens all the time and is often initiated by others.

We have found it necessary to reframe both these definitions of innovation and change and the implied approaches to their management. Research on innovation makes it clear that often the greatest inventions are not luxuries, but new responses to old problems provoked by crisis. It is also clear that although the natural tendency is to respond to pressure with familiar management approaches, there are real dangers associated with adopting 'more of the same' solutions that have been attempted before, and persisting even if they lead to failure. There are also inherent dangers in the quick response, of acting first and thinking later: 'load, fire, aim', rather than 'load, aim, fire'. As a management trainee in the motor car industry I was often told by cynical old hands 'if you can't be right be positive'.

Rather than respond to complex phenomena with simple solutions, the effective change manager might better be advised to recognise that the world will change quickly enough without blindly stabbing at the accelerator.

Definitions of change and innovation used in this book

Throughout we have used the following definition of innovation:

> 'An *innovation* is an idea, practice, or object that is perceived as new by an individual or other unit of adoption. It matters little, so far as human behaviour is concerned, whether or not an idea is "objectively" new as measured by the lapse of time since its first use or discovery. The perceived newness of the idea for the individual determines his or her reaction to it. If the idea seems new to the individual, it is an innovation.' (Rogers, 1983 p. 11)
>
> Thus the new idea may be:
>
> a synthesis of old ideas;
>
> the adoption of an idea from others;
>
> the development of a unique approach.
>
> To some degree, it is a challenge to the present order.

These definitions deliberately separate innovation from originality, an association that we have found people commonly attach to the idea of innovation. For a new way of working to spread throughout an organisation or wider community or, to use the research jargon, for an 'innovation to diffuse', it has to become less and less 'original' as more people adopt it. The crucial issue is that it is 'new' to those adopting it. In practice, we have found that most innovations in the human services field need to be 'reinvented' to meet each new set of circumstances. However, to define 'innovation' so that it is synonymous with a completely new invention means that by definition innovations can never be adopted by others. By the definitions of innovation used here the changes that the social services director was referring to above all include several 'innovations'.

Defining 'change' is to risk getting into deep philosophical water. We will follow the advice of Wittgenstein and not dwell on what the word 'really means' but describe how the word is used. This is also difficult because many of the writers in the field, like most people, vary the way that they use the word to fit the context within which they are using it.

When the word is being used in the context of the 'management of change' it often refers to the process of quite large scale transformations of organisations and their outputs: the introduction of market principles into the National Health Service, the implementation of the community care reforms, for instance. In this book we will use the noun *'change'* to refer to such transformations.

'Change' is also often used as a verb to refer to actions throughout the process of the development and the adoption of a new idea, or to refer to altering practices and methods, and the 'reorganisation', or 'restructuring' of organisations. The terms 'reforming', 'revolutionising', and 'improving' may also be used in this sense, but have evaluative connotations and so will be avoided in this book where possible.

The word *'develop'* will be used to refer to processes where the activities build upon each other; where an innovation crystallises from loosely connected ideas into an identifiable process or product and matures as its use unfolds and as its application becomes more widespread. It is not implied that all development is good; cancer develops as do its cures.

Revisiting the distinction between managing change and managing innovation

We have said that we saw managing change and managing

innovation as different enterprises, differing in scale if not essentially different in nature. But as this approach has evolved it has become clearer that 'to reorganise' is 'to introduce innovations', into all the components that make up the new organisation. *The 'management of innovations' is then a way of approaching 'the management of change'.*

We refer to this approach as *'Managing Change Through Innovation' (MCTI)* to stress that *innovations in management are often required to produce innovations in the practice of staff.*

It is necessary to break down a change of policy and organisation into its component innovations. For instance within the community care 'changes' there are many innovations, such as preparing community care plans, introducing 'needs-led assessments' and care management, promoting user involvement in different situations, separating purchaser from provider functions, developing complaints procedures, devolving resource management, and so on.

> Different innovations have to be managed differently.

Separating innovations in this way is an essential planning exercise because different innovations need to be managed in different ways. We will see that analysing specific innovations enables managers to recognise the specific actions that have to be taken: who has to do what with whom and how the innovation relates to other events and the context that the managers are working in.

> Managing and planning change involves differentiating between the complex, interrelated elements concerned, and making connections between people and the different changes taking place.

It is necessary to identify specific innovations within large scale changes in policy so that particular action can be planned to maximise the chances of each new dimension of practice being implemented. The introduction of systems thinking and the growing interest management writers have shown in 'the culture' of the organisation has colluded with beliefs that the management of change is inevitably accompanied by the wholesale restructuring of organisations. This perpetuates the problems briefly referred to here as the 'restructuring fallacy' (see Chapter 3).

Schaffer and Thompson (1992) have criticised such corporate change programmes. They argue that managers adopting programmes such as Total Quality Management:

> '... will continue to spend vast resources on a variety of activities, only to watch cynicism grow in the ranks. And eventually management will discard many potentially useful improvement processes because it expected the impossible of them and came up empty handed.'

(Schaffer and Thompson, 1992 p.18)

This concurs with our view that many of the ways in which innovations have been introduced have actually inoculated organisations against good ideas and improved ways of working.

An introductory exercise

At this point you may wish to reflect on the ways in which you think practice changes.

We have found the following exercise a helpful way of approaching these issues. At the beginning of many of our Managing Change Through Innovation workshops we asked participants to note on a piece of paper or yellow 'post it' 'something that changed their practice, either in their professional role, or as a manager. We stick the 'post its' up on the wall. Then we asked them to write on a green 'post it' a brief note on 'how does your organisation set about changing the practice of its staff? Participants are then invited to compare and contrast their experience with their colleagues and the two lists.

PRACTICE CHANGES You may like to try this now:

What experiences changed your practice?

✍

How does your organisation attempt to change the practice of its staff?

✍

In our workshops the two lists have always been significantly different although there has been some overlap around training experiences and major redefinition of role. Typically people say that they changed the way they work because of some direct experience which was personally significant. Most people say that their organisations attempt to change practice through declarations of policy changes and changing procedures. Almost all are subject to various dimensions of reorganisation, with, but often without some attempt at 'consultation'. Some say they are offered 'training'. We can not recall this ever being called 're-training'. Framed in this way most people feel *subject* to their organisation's approaches to change management and not involved in them.

CHAPTER TWO

The Simple Linear Model

*'There is always an easy solution to every
human problem - neat, easy and wrong'*
(H.L. Mencken)

Having ideas, introducing new methods of work, formulating
and implementing new policies - all are processes which rarely
follow a straightforward path. This is in contrast to the 'rational'
approach to research and development which does follow such
a path: an idea is conceived and put into practice at a test site; it
is evaluated and research results published; if the evidence
suggests that the practice is successful, then it is taken up by
many and adopted as official policy.

Maybe this is what should happen, but research on the diffusion
of innovations clearly illustrates that, in practice, this is rarely
the case. Often the innovations that get adopted are those that
are *adoptable*, despite the evidence on their effectiveness, and
the process is rarely simple and straightforward. The route
taken by a new method, from idea to widespread
implementation, is often down a road full of bumps, twists and
bends, brick walls, U-turns and tangential changes of direction.

It would not matter if the failure of simple linear models simply
meant that life was more complex than elegant ideas. The main
problem of the fallacies, as we have called them, is that
appropriate action is not planned and managed, and people are
encouraged to identify the wrong causes when the assumed
path of change is interrupted. The consequences can be
extremely costly. It would be convenient to have a simple,
elegant model for managing change. However, the processes of
successfully changing practice, of getting people to adopt
innovations is complex and takes time.

You may feel, as you read on, that the approach outlined here is
too long and complicated to undertake, that there has to be an
easier way. Restructuring the organisation, rewriting policy,
delivering new instructions and assuming implementation
through obedience will seem like an attractive option for those
of you who manage those you want to change. If you can

guarantee compliance, and not just superficial obedience, this may be the best option, and you do not need to read this book!

Restructuring departments and services is easy. Policy makers advocate it and senior managers do it all the time. We are reminded of the addicted smoker who says: 'Giving up smoking? No problem; I do it often'. But making a difference to practice means changing people's behaviour and the relationships between them. It means learning new ways and constantly checking progress, guarding against slippage back into old habits and long established patterns of relationships.

Revolutions are swift and dramatic events; the major players often become famous. Redistributing power in any society has never been achieved so quickly. Any vandal will tell you how quickly they can take things apart; few builders will offer to make good the damage on the same time scale.

Those of you who are aware that you do not control all of the actions of all of the people who need to change in order to implement practice and service delivery changes will have to struggle with an approach to change management which is as complex as the processes involved.

> Changes in practice come about through 'convergent thinking' and 'contagious processes'.

A 'simple linear' model for the dissemination of a new method of practice assumes that information passes from its source, typically from an 'expert' or the policy makers at the top of an organisation, to others who are either open to information and instructions or 'resistant' to change. We know, however, from the fields of adult learning, cognitive psychology and research on the diffusion of innovations, that these processes are much more complex. In practice new ideas 'converge' with, or diverge from, the ideas that people already have (Rogers and Kincaid, 1981; Rogers, 1995).

People have their own ideas, beliefs and knowledge; they are not passive or neutral receivers waiting for messages. The communicators', in practice, enter into dialogues with people who interpret messages in accordance with their own views and beliefs which may or may not be the same as the communicators. Those sending communications may be clear about what they intend to say, but they should never make assumptions about what the other person receives. In their 'own mind' those receiving a message will hear what the message means to them: they will understand or not, agree or disagree with the communication, and then react, which may or may not be overtly consistent with what they think. Communication across ethnic, racial, class, professional or other cultural boundaries needs particular care if preconceived assumptions and prejudices are not going to lead to misunderstanding or worse.

You have your own ideas about managing change. Reading this you will be comparing and contrasting them with the ideas we describe. You will not adopt all that you read here. You may accept some of the ideas, use some of the suggestions, see some things differently and have a better approach as a result. The people who have found these ideas most helpful have been successful innovators. They have typically recognised the ideas as the ones that they have used themselves, even if they have never put them into words.

Finally, experience of working with innovatory managers and practitioners over the years suggests that a 'simple linear' model is inadequate in another major dimension: it not only oversimplifies reality, it distorts it. Although researchers have disagreed as to the wisdom of modifying innovations, most recognise that adaptation is not only inevitable, it is desirable and even essential. The benefit of reinvention may be that rather than simply accepting or rejecting an innovation, potential adopters actively strive to give it meaning in a local context. The distinction between invention, and adopting innovations produced elsewhere, is then blurred, the latter also requiring creative thought and management.

> There will always be at least an element of reinvention when innovations are adapted to fit the next situation.
>
> For many innovations it is more important that ideas and concepts are communicated rather than full prescriptions for practice. The ideas of roundness and axles may be more helpful than fully designed wheels.

The simple linear model also fails to recognise that people rarely adopt new practices, that is change their behaviour, through a kind of religious conversion. We will see, as we describe the different dimensions of managing change, that most people change practice through contact with other people who sell or demonstrate the idea. Saint Paul may have been converted by a blinding light, but most people rely on picking up new ways of doing things through contact with other people, through what we might appropriately call a contagious process.

We have said that we suspect that much so-called resistance to change is not that people are fighting the proposed new method to blindly maintain the status quo. Those resisting a change are often just as keenly aware of a need for reform as others but often have their own ideas about how it should be done.

> Often 'resistance' is the natural reaction of people to change agent activity based on the 'simple rational' model of change.

People constantly fail in their attempts to replicate innovations and to turn them from pioneering projects into mainstream practice because they think that the process is too simple.

> It is a fallacy to think that innovations can simply be transferred and replicated. To replicate innovations, or to turn them into mainstream practice, change managers have to copy what has been done to arrive at the innovation – not just the innovation itself.

CHAPTER THREE

Inoculation and Managing Change Fallacies

Many agencies are inoculated against new methods of work and approaches to service delivery by the way that change is managed.

Before finding out how the process of introducing innovations works we need to clear out of the way the numerous misunderstandings that have arisen about the theory and practice of the process. Only when we understand what does *not* work, and why, can we begin to move towards a new approach.

Most of us have implicit or explicit theories about the way change should be managed. During our work on the NISW project we found that many of these 'models' turned out to be fallacies when set alongside the available evidence on how innovations take hold. In this chapter we will discuss some of the most common fallacies in order to illustrate the value of developing a rigorous approach to managing change. We have divided the fallacies into three groups.

1. THE TELL AND DO NOTHING FALLACIES:

CASCADE

ANTHROPOMORPHIC

NATURAL SELECTION

TROJAN HORSE or START WITH A PILOT PROJECT

The Cascade fallacy

The 'cascade principle' is a common metaphor used to describe how to transfer new ideas and policies into organisations. It goes like this: top managers are introduced to a new idea and as a result the desired changes automatically flow down through the organisation. But it does not seem to work like this in practice: far from a cascade effect many organisations recognise what they call the 'trickle-down effect'. For instance, a social services director, speaking on the implementation of recent social policy changes, claimed that he and his senior management team had adopted the values of the National Health Service and Community Care Act, but he thought that it would take another five years for it to *filter down* through the whole of his department.

Given the widespread acceptance of this model the research literature on innovations is remarkably sparse on the subject. Computer searches uncovered only two linked research studies: neither demonstrated the effectiveness of the model.

The Anthropomorphic fallacy

It is common to talk of 'new methods developing', of 'ideas spreading', of 'innovations diffusing', as if they somehow did this by themselves. The use of language in this way can mislead us into thinking that there is a force for change that does not require action from those who would have that change come about. J.K. Galbraith, in a recent discussion of forecasts for the end of economic recession, has warned us against such phenomenon in the world of economics. Referring to the predictions of what 'the economy' was about to do he says:

> 'In all this, one central idea, or what could be so described, is foremost. The economic system has within itself a personified power for recovery. This is firmly stated: "The economy," one reads, "is now wrestling with the final stages of recession"... The time has come to - has long since passed - for an end to this nonsense. The present recession is not an autonomous, self correcting economic drama. It is the wholly predictable response to the speculative extravagances and insanities (and the government policies) of the eighties.'

(Galbraith, 1991).

The Natural Selection fallacy

Many of us have an implicit belief in the 'march of progress' and assume that innovation and change are, by definition, progress. Applying this theory we conclude that the 'best' innovations are the ones adopted and that the ineffective fall by the wayside. If the 'best' means those innovations which hard research evidence tells us achieved desired outcomes, then this is not the case. Unfortunately, good research evidence does not guarantee adoption.

In 1601 an English sea captain carried out an experiment and demonstrated that scurvy could be prevented by giving sailors three teaspoonfuls of lemon juice every day. Scurvy, at this time, killed more sailors on long sea voyages than warfare, accidents, and all other causes of death. One hundred and fifty years later a British Navy physician confirmed these findings, but it still took another forty-eight years before the British Navy eradicated scurvy by adopting the idea of supplying citrus fruits for scurvy prevention in 1795. The merchant marine had to wait another seventy years and suffer an unknown number of deaths (probably between a half to two-thirds of all long voyage sailors), before the Board of Trade adopted a similar policy in 1865. This was two hundred and sixty four years after the first empirical proof of the solution. (Mosteller, 1981)

There are many current examples of the same processes, despite the wide acceptance of the value of science. It is just as true that an innovation can be adopted even when research shows that it is ineffective or even harmful.

The Trojan Horse or Start With a Pilot Project fallacy

Another widely held belief is that innovations can be introduced into agencies through pilot projects. It is true that pilot projects can play an important role in the development of innovations. The fallacy is in believing that the good elements of the project's experience will be naturally sustained and adopted by others while the bad fall into disuse. After all, the Trojans were not beaten by the horse but by the invading Greeks let into the city by the hidden soldiers.

'Special' projects can attract considerable resentment from others in the mainstream of the organisation, especially if the project workers are released from statutory duties or given extra resources. For example, Newburn (1993) describes how the teams set up to respond to the Hillsborough disaster experienced growing resentment from former colleagues and managers the longer their separate work went on. We suspect that these feelings make it more difficult for mainstream staff to learn from the experience of others, particularly 'prophets in their own country.'

Working with innovatory practitioners in situations such as these, we found that *organisations can be inoculated against innovation*. While people on pilot projects are developing their new form of practice, others in the organisation are working out how they are going to avoid working in the same way. Managers, whose commitment to the innovation is vital for widespread adoption, may give initial approval to the innovation without working through the implications of committing the organisation to full adoption. When managers get to the point where they attempt to generalise from the experience of the pilot project, others in the organisation are ready with their counter arguments.

We should remember the Greeks won the war because the soldiers hidden in the horse opened the gates to let in the rest of the invading army. No matter how much we learn from pilot projects we need other strategies for disseminating results and achieving wide spread change.

These fallacies could be grouped under a single heading the *Tell and Do Nothing* fallacies because they all erroneously assume that there is some natural force at work. They are at best only half truths: although some elements may work, further action is required to make changes happen rather than relying on the hidden forces assumed in these models.

We now move on to a different set of fallacies. These are based on erroneous assumptions about the people involved.

2. THE PEOPLE FALLACIES:

CHARISMATIC INDIVIDUALS CAUSE SUCCESS - FAILURE IS THE FAULT OF VILLAINS

PEOPLE WANT TO AVOID RE-INVENTING THE WHEEL

TO KNOW IS TO ACT DIFFERENTLY

The Charismatic Individuals fallacy And Its Corollary - Failure Is Caused By Resistant Villains

The credit for a new method is often ascribed to individual heroines or heroes. The shortage of these charismatic individuals is often blamed for a failure to replicate innovations. Conversely, the absence of such people in failed attempts to innovate is often cited as evidence of the significance of these 'special' people. It is beyond the scope of this book to discuss the nature of charisma, but, long ago, Freud, describing *Civilisation and its Discontents*, drew attention to the dangers of believing that 'charisma' was a characteristic of particular individuals. He suggested that it was a shared characteristic of the beholders rather than a personal attribute of the subject.

> We should heed Mark Twain who pointed out that: 'A person with a new idea is a crank, until the idea succeeds'.

In the charisma analysis those who obstruct the adoption of a good idea must be villains, if not actively malignant, then at least ignorant, or stupid, or dominated by self interest, or all three. Although he has reservations about the term, Everett Rogers (1983) continues to refer to those who are last to adopt an innovation as 'laggards'. However, he has also argued that it is wrong simply to see these people as personally responsible for their lack of openness to innovation. After further analysis of the diffusion research he concludes that the failure of 'laggards' to adopt a beneficial innovation is a product of the diffusion system: the result of their position in the communication network that fails to transmit the innovation. In short, they adopt last because they are the last to be told about the innovation.

The People Want To Avoid Re-inventing the Wheel fallacy

The National Institute for Social Work's Practice And Development Exchange (PADE) was established to exchange information between innovatory practitioners, managers and researchers. Together they worked on developing better models of practice and management through a synthesis of their knowledge. We made the assumption at the beginning of our work that there were many people attempting to develop solutions to the same practice and management problems.

The 'reinvention of the wheel' cliché appeared in most of our early reports and publicity to help explain the purpose of PADE. Conventional wisdom suggested that people reinvented wheels because they lacked access to relevant information and knowledge about who was doing what where. Both are important factors, but we quickly found that the transfer of information was a complex process and the simple belief that people wanted to avoid reinventing the wheel was a fallacy.

In fact, many feel that it is cheating to get ideas from others, while other people clearly want to invent their own practice. Researchers in the field have dubbed this the Not Invented Here (NIH) syndrome. Exchanges can work, but it is not a simple process as will be seen from the approach presented here.

The To Know Is To Act Differently fallacy

Those introducing innovations and managers making changes in policy often assume that once a change in ideas has been communicated or a decision made to adopt a new policy, then a new approach to practice will automatically follow. Many managers would probably agree, at least in principle, that it is important to get their staff to 'own' a new way of working and that it is necessary to be clear what is required of them to practice in a different way. They might think that this is enough. Many underestimate the difficulties involved in changing what people do. Consider the relationship between the availability of staff development and expectations of subsequent practice changes. Staff are often expected to be able to undertake new, complex forms of practice after only a few days training, or even in response to the introduction of a new set of procedures or practice guidelines. In some situations short training courses will work and co-operative staff will be able to comply with new directives. However, evidence suggests that practice cannot always change in this way, and that more extensive staff development activities are required.

Chris Argyris, in his work on improving individual and organisational behaviour, illustrated that trainee consultants found it difficult not to practice the opposite of what they preached. He set up a situation where they were invited to respond to the way that a supervisor was commenting on a member of staff's performance. When criticising the supervision they frequently replicated the behaviour they deplored in others. It was indeed common for people to demonstrate that they operated on a 'do as I say', not a 'do as I do', basis. (Argyris, 1982). This does not just happen through hypocrisy. The main problems seem to be a lack of awareness of the need to behave differently and limited behaviour repertoires to draw on.

Such beliefs are a major way in which departments are inoculated against an innovation. It is assumed that practice has changed after new management prescriptions have been declared, brief training undertaken, and the best intentions of staff have been gained. Staff themselves believe that their own intention to behave in a different way is translated into practice despite maintaining many of their old habits. The innovation is subsequently judged without having actually been applied. As we have stressed before with other myths, there is also some truth in the 'to know is to act differently' fallacy. It is important to be able to distinguish between those innovations that can be introduced through a new prescription and those that cannot.

The next group of fallacies further illustrate the necessity for analysing the nature of the change being introduced.

3. THE INNOVATION FALLACIES:

INNOVATION IS ALWAYS PROGRESS

ALL INNOVATIONS ARE ADDITIONS

MORE OF THE SAME

NEW WAYS OF WORKING HAVE TO BE LED BY RESTRUCTURING

The Innovation Is Always Progress fallacy

People are often biased towards the view that since all innovations are good, they should be adopted by all members of a social system, be diffused more rapidly, and be neither re-invented nor rejected. In practice the unquestioning acceptance of innovation as always beneficial is dangerous. The diffusion of bottle-feeding among poor mothers in the Third World is one of many examples of an innovation that, while advantageous for its advocates and some people, has had disastrous consequences for the many adopters.

So called 'laggards', rather than being open to criticism for their lack of acceptance of an innovation, may actually be right, having perceived the disadvantages of the proposal, or because they are champions of a competing practice.

The All Innovations Are Additions fallacy

It is common to assume that all new approaches to practice and service delivery can only be introduced if new resources can be found to add on the new form of practice to existing work. 'Innovatory work' is often seen as a 'luxury' compared to the work that is defined as 'real work' by the status quo. In business it is often tempting to distribute profits rather than re-invest. In the personal social services a limited reading of the various Acts of Parliament and Department of Health guidance can cause only parts of the spectrum to be seen as essential work. (We might call this the 'what about the statutory work?' syndrome). Another assumption is that innovations are an optional extra promoted by interested staff seeking new experiences.

It is true that new responsibilities are placed on departments and that new areas of work arise, requiring more resources. But, of course, many innovations are replacements for current ways of working. This sometimes also requires extra resources for the management of the transition period when old and new systems run in parallel, as the new is developed to a point where it can take over.

The More Of The Same fallacy

Managers often assume that they can use well-tried management strategies to introduce new forms of practice. People understandably attempt to solve problems with 'more of the same' solutions which they believe to have worked in the past. Often this works, but there are significant exceptions. Managers may attribute innovation success to a variety of factors *other* than those indicated by hard evidence. They can assume that they are successful in introducing innovations through any of the processes that we have identified as fallacies; indeed they would not persist if this were not so. This becomes a particular problem when the way that an innovation is introduced undermines its own adoption. Some innovations are particularly prone to this confusion: for example, changes in the nature of the relationships within the organisation, such as devolved resource management; or between the organisation and others including user participation in decision making. As anti-war campaigners have pointed out: fighting for peace is like fornicating for virginity! We will return to this dilemma in Chapter 7 when discussing the significance of understanding the different order of change the innovations can cause in key relationships.

People draw on their own experience to apply solutions that have worked before, to respond to a problem with a 'more of the same' solution. People with a strong faith in the correctness of particular solutions will often persist even if the solution persistently fails. Faced with failure, people with faith, despite experience or without an alternative solution, will escalate the application of the failed solution, applying even 'more of the same'. If the failed solution adds to the problem, rather than resolving it, such strategies can prove disastrous. The application of force to counter violence, where it leads to greater violence, is a typical example.

'More of the same' also becomes a problem when the innovation, be it a solution to a problem or a product, is obsolete. The *management* of innovations is also prone to such obsolescence, making it likely that the belief in 'more of the same' management strategies to introduce change will be fallacious.

The New Ways Of Working Have To Be Led By Restructuring fallacy

Reorganisations are perhaps the most common way in which many organisations are inoculated against the adoption of innovatory forms of practice.

Managers struggle to change structure at the expense of attention to practice: the completion of the task.

In this unstable state practitioners cling on to the security of their known ways of working and fit them into the new structure.

The reorganisation is then completed, but with much of the old practice in place.

Major reorganisations and wholesale restructuring have become a continual fact of life in many organisations, particularly large companies and in the social and health services. There are many reasons why some of these changes take place. Sometimes they are undertaken through choice, often to cut costs, and sometimes under the mistaken assumption that it is an inevitable part of the process of initiating changes in front line practice. Reorganisations often ignore the fact that change takes place through a convergence of ideas, of the old and the new. Reorganisations often seem to be based on the misguided principle that you can somehow start all over again with an organisation, the way one might discard a machine to buy the latest model. More often than not reorganisation is simply assumed to be *the only way* of achieving change. If a reorganisation fails to make a difference the most common response seems to be 'more of the same', that is, further reorganisation.

We have come across few examples where senior managers have successfully identified and promoted practice within their organisations consistent with proposed reforms, such as practitioners who were using needs-led assessments or teams with a good track record in building partnerships with families and/or local organisations. We know of many examples where such work has been dismantled through reorganisations ostensibly designed to introduce the new ways of working.

> Many managers plough up the lawn to turn the whole garden over to grass.

We assume that organisations should be practice-led. By this we mean that they should be designed to achieve their fundamental tasks and not determined by the need to maintain, or enlarge the organisation, nor should they be run for the convenience of the people within them. We are doubtful of the efficacy of reorganisation-led change as a strategy for practice improvement. Our review of the literature reinforces this scepticism. For example Rosabeth Moss-Kanter's (1989) research into the impact of corporate take-overs identifies major problems caused by large scale reorganisations. These include the 'three D's':

- Discontinuity: gaps between what was once appropriate and what will now be appropriate - until the next change;
- Disorder: uncertainty about what should be done and the standards to apply;
- Distraction: the diversion of people's attention from the tasks of the organisation.

Managers have important immediate tasks to perform and decisions to make, but during reorganisations they are called away for meetings and are often caught up in secret deliberations. At the same time leaders may be less available to counter the 'three D's'. They are so swamped by decisions about what to do that they simply do not have the time or attention for process matters such as the observation of how things are going. We have continually been told that managers cannot get involved in developing their ability to manage change and innovation because they are in the middle of a reorganisation!

It is especially ironic that more commitment is needed at the very time when the basis for commitment itself is temporarily weakened. The difficulties restructuring can make for the organisation to retain its values, and the threats to current productivity have been described as follows:

The cost of confusion: from small details, such as people not being able to find things, not knowing their own telephone extensions, to staff not understanding their new roles and how they relate to others;

Misinformation: communication is haphazard, and some managers do a better job than others of keeping their people informed. Rumours are created and take on a life of their own, especially when it is not clear what was the 'right' information, and some of the rumours are potentially destructive;

Emotional leakage: managers are so focused on the reorganisation tasks to be done and decisions to be made that they neglect or ignore the emotional reactions engendered by the changes. But the reactions leak out anyway, sometimes in unusual behaviour;

Loss of energy: any change consumes emotional energy - especially if the restructuring is perceived negatively. People become preoccupied with the current situation. They feel guilt about the people who are losing something. The mood becomes sombre, morale sinks, and it is hard to maintain the usual pace of work. For example:

'It's very hard to work when you have no idea what will happen next. "Final" changes are replaced by new ones every other week. So even when you're told you survived a "final" round of cuts, you know you can still get another turn next month. No one can really know what's coming down at his level until they settle who's where on the top floors.'

'Right now it's so chaotic you can be demoted if you stay on, but also called disloyal if you go for the exit package. Most of the people leaving looked relaxed, like now they can stop worrying about what's happening here. The ones who can't get out or want to stay anyway are the most nervous and upset.'

(Quoted from Moss-Kanter, 1989)

One of the costs of reorganisation is the loss of staff who do not like the way the change is managed and leave. Those who are good at their job are often the ones who can get another job easily. This 'cost' to the organisation is often underestimated. Major reorganisation also stops innovation not only because senior management is too preoccupied with the reorganisation, but also because key people who promote innovations have been moved elsewhere, leaving vacancies which cannot be filled because of the uncertainty of the reorganisation.

It seems particularly strange to come across organisations 're-engineering' to develop themselves as a 'learning organisation' by getting rid of staff with much experience and expertise. Do learning organisations really 'learn' by wiping the memory of the organisation and starting again?

All of this is not to argue that organisations should never be restructured. Some innovations are in themselves 'reorganisations', for example devolved resource management. Many innovations will have organisational consequences that provoke some level of reorganisation.

The point is that a practice-led organisation develops innovations, that is changes the details of practice, as it manages the consequences of such changes for the way that the public, staff and management should relate to each other. Instead of occasional massive restructuring of organisations as if they were machines to be rebuilt, managers should be constantly adapting their organisations in the way that the gardener tends her land and living plants. This metaphor contrasts with the more common mechanistic metaphor of organisations in the minds of many managers. Of course, some gardeners are brutal diggers, cutters and pruners - but they tend not to have oak trees growing in the right places. We are reminded of the gardener of a Tudor house in York who, asked by an American tourist how he got such a good lawn replied 'Oh, just by cutting and rolling it'. The American said, 'But I've done that since I laid a new lawn last year'. Replied the gardener, 'Ah, you have to do it regularly over four hundred years'.

The directorate and senior management team of one organisation we worked with crystallised the problem. They all declared that they were engaged in managing change in their organisation, but only one said that he was involved in changing practice. As the director said at the time: *'Then what on earth are the rest of us doing it for?'*

Avoid 'killing the patient'

All of the 'models' that we have described as fallacies have elements of truth in them and will sometimes be followed by desired outcomes. A rain dance is sometimes followed by rain. No approach to managing change can enable managers always to obtain their desired results; there will always be factors beyond the control of the major actors that will change the course of planned change. But an approach for managing change should increase the probability of change in the desired direction, improve on chance and reduce some of the counter-productive consequences outlined above. The way that change is managed should not inoculate the organisation against the innovation it is intended to introduce, just as surgery should not kill the patient.

Conclusion

Finally we have pointed out that there is a pro-innovation bias in the literature and in most of our minds. To counter this, and to summarise the major points of this chapter, managers may want to consider the following. Participants in our development programmes have agreed that when confronted with an innovation they do not want to implement, a useful approach is to 'STALL':

To inoculate your organisation against an innovation:

STALL

S et up a pilot project to debug the innovation:

This buys time, and enables you either to evaluate before the innovation could prove effective, or to wait for results until the innovation is obsolete. The main advantage, however, is that it enables the bulk of the organisation to work out why the innovation cannot be adopted by them.

T ell them to change in writing:

Draft new guidelines/procedures/instructions. You demonstrate that you have adopted the innovation and that failure is their fault, or the innovations or both. You are protected from criticisms and it is rarely enough to get them to change their practice even if they want to; change what you say but not what you do.

A dd the innovation to custom and practice:

Do not introduce new resources, but even if you do they are likely to be absorbed by the status quo unless you stop old practices.

L eave dissemination to natural forces:

Either through the formal channels of communication down the hierarchy or the logic of the innovation's advantages; keep training short and based on individuals; don't give staff time to exchange ideas.

L ead through reorganisation:

This also buys considerable time. It has the added advantages of providing you with the opportunity of getting rid of difficult staff and giving the others an example of what could happen to them if they forget whose boss.

CHAPTER FOUR

Managing Change Through Managing Innovation: Towards an Alternative Approach

Basic assumptions of this approach

Our developing approach is based on an awareness of the complexity of social situations and the impossibility, even undesirability, of any one person or small group of people being in control of all the variables that affect and direct change. The recognition that change takes place relative to other changes in the social and physical context is central to this approach. The aim is to go with compatible changes and not to constantly struggle against resistance. This approach involves analysing the major changes taking place to identify the discrete innovations involved. This not only makes thinking about the total problem more manageable but highlights how different parts of the change have to be handled, or managed differently. This is not a recommendation to split up complex changes by segmentalising organisations into specialist units. It is a prescription for detailed planning and differentiated action based on a better understanding of what needs to be done.

What is the problem?

> The opening transactions between those managing innovations and others will be to initiate a 'convergence' of thinking about the nature of the problem that the innovation is an attempt to resolve.

Not everybody will see the status quo as a problem. Indeed some will see the innovation as 'a problem'. This is made more likely if an innovation is introduced ahead of a consensus about the nature of 'the problem'. We are reminded here of Charles Handy's first injunction to managers introducing change:

'Create an awareness of the need for change. Preferably not by argument or rationale but by exposure to objective fact.'

(Handy, 1981)

Seeing innovation as solutions to problems

We have found it helpful to frame innovations as solutions to problems. This enables us to recognise that the problem addressed by the innovation may not be a high priority problem, or even a problem at all for major actors in the situation; that the solution may not be other people's chosen solution even if they agree with the definition of the problem.

> Much so called resistance to change can be understood as negative feedback to change agents about:
>
> - their definition of the problem;
> - their chosen solution; and,
> - the way that they are managing change.
>
> To introduce 'solutions' to people who do not perceive themselves as having a problem will not unreasonably be seen as imposing a gratuitous burden, or at least an inconvenient interruption in their work.
>
> To introduce a solution that is not seen as related to the problem as the people involved define it themselves, is reasonably seen as an irrelevance.
>
> To introduce a solution without people being able to see how it will solve the problem requires people to trust the innovation and/or the innovator.

Trust is an important commodity in the management of change. Nobody can be certain that an innovation will 'work'. If we know anything about the processes of innovation and change it is that they are unpredictable and cause anxiety. It is then vital that those managing change do everything that they can to establish their credibility to develop the trust of those who need to put faith in the innovation.

The fact that many will want change, even when they have different definitions of the problems that need to be addressed and competing solutions, enables us to recognise the possibilities for *'convergence'* in thinking between the change agent and others. It also helps us to assess the potential for *'divergence'* between significant people. Another way of framing this is to recognise *'allies'* and *'opponents'* and the potential for building 'synergy' with complementary innovations and directions of change.

Framing innovation as a problem solving process also has the following consequences:

1. It enables the innovator to *keep the purpose of changing things in the forefront of their minds, rather than just 'the innovation'*. It is unhelpful to focus on the innovation alone and judge success only in terms of the adoption or application of the innovation. It is dangerous if the innovation becomes a cause in its own right. *'Success' is not the adoption of an 'innovation'. Success lies in finding effective solutions to our problems*. It is necessary for the evaluation of 'change' or of an 'innovation' to consider the consequences of our interventions, not just the short term objective of applying a particular solution.

2. It encourages us to focus on the purpose of change. Keeping it tightly defined helps us *avoid changing more than necessary*

3. It helps us to recognise that *negotiation over 'what needs to change and how'* is a better starting point than selling a definition of the problem and a pre-chosen solution.

Seen as solutions to problems, innovations can be:

- a better solution, an improvement on existing practices or equipment;
- a new solution to an old problem;
- a new solution to a new problem;
- a solution to an old problem that does not have so many harmful, unintended consequences

Innovations are often some combination of all these different descriptions.

Innovations are often seen as one kind of solution to some of those involved and have another purpose for others.

The innovation of opening community based accommodation for mental health patients and closing large mental hospitals was a professional solution to the side effects of institutionalisation to some; the resolution of a human rights issues for those who advocated 'normalisation' in living arrangements for people previously excluded from the community; and a cost saving exercise for others. For some at the heart of these processes they represented a massive, unnecessary disruption - and were not seen as solutions at all.

Addressing the right problem

The status quo can also be seen as the way in which problems are being solved.

Recognising this enables us to see that where the innovation addresses the unintended consequences of an existing solution it must also address the original problem to succeed. To effectively introduce innovatory alternatives to residential care we have to be clear how we are solving the problems that residential care was a solution to, that is, the anxiety of those who recognised the risks to people under-supported in the community.

Many of our most difficult, persistent problems are perpetuated because some people get the benefits of the problems solved by maintaining the status quo, and it is others who suffer from the unintended consequences. It is often not difficult to find motivation to change amongst those who are suffering. But why should we expect those whose problems are being solved to change?

Many managers have 'the innovation' chosen for them by policy makers. They then have to work out how to apply the innovation in their situation. This will include considering the degree to which it is both necessary and possible to reinvent the innovation, and the direction such reinvention should take. This will depend upon their initial mapping of their circumstances (see Chapter 5).

Whenever possible, the change manager will review and change the solutions to be applied, making sure that they:

- address 'the problem' as defined by the key players;
- build on and, where possible, marry up with the solutions that all players would see as possible and desirable;
- build on and dovetail with the old solutions that you need to keep in place.

Wherever possible you should add to the 'normal' way of solving problems for the people involved. To introduce 'foreign' solutions from a different problem solving culture is either to be avoided or entered into consciously and then managed appropriately. It is necessary to understand and learn from others to engage in a 'convergence' of ideas across cultural boundaries. To assume that one culture should simply replace another is to risk the dangers of colonisation at the expense of creative convergence.

Working with the vision and the mission of the organisation

We found that many of the most successful innovators had a clear vision of what kind of service they wanted to deliver. In the personal social services, the community social work innovators of the 1980s were a good example of such people. They were markedly different from their colleagues for three major reasons.

First, they held a certain group of clear, shared principles. In addition to more widely held values about good practice they believed that:

- services must be accessible to people in terms of the times of the day and week, and as near as possible to where they lived;
- services should not be stigmatising - people should not have to be labelled as 'clients' before they received help and support;
- all people in the neighbourhood, including those traditionally only seen as 'clients', were seen as potential sources of support;

- the role of the professional was to link up those with resources to those with particular needs at a particular time, rather than assume that they would themselves always provide the service;

- social situations, that is family and neighbourhood networks, were seen as the focus of help, support, problem resolution or management and change, and not just individuals who 'had' or 'were' problems;

- service users were to be involved in decision making about their lives as fully as possible and also involved in service planning;

- team work, both within the agency and across agency boundaries, was seen as essential, just as the 'problems' were recognised as involving the relationships between identified service users and others, so the relationships between people attempting to help were seen as crucial to problem resolution or management.

The second difference was the way they applied these values. They took them literally and went out into their community looking for ways to apply them - to use some of the jargon of the day, *they were 'proactive' rather than 'reactive'.* A key example of this difference was the way that they would encourage people to tell them of those who had problems, and find ways of helping others to respond. They would also regularly visit schools to see if there were families that needed help, but had not yet reached the point of formal referral. They would then seek to link them up to people who could help without formally taking them on as 'clients'.

The third difference was that these innovators applied these solutions in many different ways. They used them as 'guiding principles' around which they constantly improvised. They seemed to constantly change their practice to fit the specific circumstances they found themselves in rather than follow prescriptions for practice, such as particular methods of intervention, say, family therapy or task centred casework. *They were problem solving: innovating, or re-innovating rather than applying a particular innovation no matter what the circumstances.*

It is worth noting in passing that we have worked with many practitioners and leading change managers for the last fifteen years without 'stress' and 'burnout' ever appearing as issues of concern. Overwork was often a problem. But it seems that seeking out and addressing problems, even if you find too many, is better than waiting and being bombarded by them. We discuss the importance of initiative for change agents in chapter 6, but we should never forget that:

> Those taking the initiative find change more palatable than those being changed by others.

For large scale innovations the change managers and the senior management team will need to demonstrate their commitment to the vision of change. This does not mean that the vision is a fixed, detailed set of prescriptions, but that managers will demonstrate a clear sense of direction, working out the complete vision with others as changes progress.

CHANGE MANAGERS SHOULD CONSIDER:

- How does the innovation fulfil the organisation's mission and contribute to its major aims?

  ✍

- How does it fit with the change manager's vision of good practice?

  ✍

- How does this vision 'fit' with the prevailing conventional wisdom about good practice?

  ✍

- How does it match service users' perceptions of what they want and need?

  ✍

CHAPTER FIVE

Level One: The Foundations of Change. What changes – What stays the same

'Think hard before forming an ambition - you may achieve it!'
(Chinese Proverb)

Mapping change and innovation

The first step in the process of managing change is to draw up a map of all the people involved in the path of changing practice, that is all those who need to participate in the implementation of innovations. This enables 'change managers' to begin to identify the significant people, reflect on their attitudes to the application of the particular targeted innovation and to recognise that there are more people involved than initially anticipated. Mapping is central to identifying who has to do what and with whom. It is possible to draw up a list of critical activities, or negotiations, based on recognising key people, where they 'stand' on the innovation now, what they need to be doing for the innovation to be implemented, what relationships need to change, and so on. We will return to these maps, modify and add to them at each level of activity described as this approach unfolds.

Maps will be constantly changing. In practice it is difficult to predict where people will be standing until you interact with them and then your map will change. Also the people on the map will change over time. However, the process of working out how you can manage change begins with:

MAPPING I

Draw up a map of the significant people that you identify through reflection on:

- the innovation that you want to introduce;
- the problem that it addresses;
- the people involved in the status quo that it replaces.

Maps should include *all* the people involved or affected by the status quo - and by change.

This map is then used to lay the foundations for the process of managing change by first identifying 'the problem', or more precisely 'who sees what as a problem?'.

MAP I

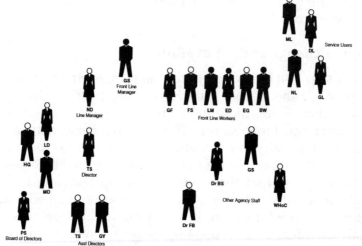

IDENTIFY 'THE PROBLEM':

- For whom is the status quo a problem?
  ✍

- Who wants change and for what reasons?
  ✍

- How do the service users or customers see the problem?
  ✍

Change managers will be looking at *all* the people in the path of the innovation. They will be attempting to identify and reconcile different definitions of the problem and its possible solutions, i.e. appropriate innovations. Service users, whether social service users, health service patients or commercial companies' customers are crucial key players. There are two reasons for underlining this when managing change. The first and obvious one is that the service has to be relevant to the people it is designed to serve. If they do not see the innovation as a solution to their problems we have to question the validity of its introduction. In the health and social services this is the relatively new area of service user participation. In the commercial world there is a longer tradition of market research. The second reason for identifying this dimension is because the service user can also be an agent for innovation and change.

Major ideas change when a new piece of information enters into a field and does not fit with the conventional wisdom. In science, a new discovery may add new knowledge but occasionally the new observation does not fit existing theory. The old knowledge and the new observation can only fit if the underlying theory - the paradigm - shifts. The growing voice of the service user is often such an agent of change. They are outside of the provider system and so they will see problems and potential solutions from a 'new' perspective. The mobilisation of this voice by change managers is often an important part of introducing change in the system. The convergence of thinking between the ideas of the would-be innovator and the service user is a crucial dimension of making sure that the innovations introduced are appropriate, i.e. those relevant to the resolution of the problems that the organisation exists to serve.

CHANGES AND INNOVATIONS

- What changes are required to tackle the problem?

  (In this context 'change' refers to broad ideas about solutions to problems, how the mission of the organisation and the tasks could be more effectively achieved, how people's circumstances could be improved.)

  ✍

- What are the innovations involved in the proposed changes? (An 'innovation' is a specific practice, method, technology or form of service delivery new to those to whom it is being introduced).

  ✍

- Begin to invent and reinvent innovations appropriate to local circumstances.

  ✍

Persistance and change

All things change but some things are more stable than others.

It is misleading and unhelpful to constantly stress that everything changes all the time. It may well be true that a butterfly beating its wings in one part of the globe sets off a chain of linked events that leads to a hurricane in another, but this knowledge, or rather theory, does not yet lead to practical intervention. It is also true that all is flux and that nothing stays the same but the relativity of change is all important.

The relationship between persistence and change is of the utmost importance in the management of the process.

Changing more than needs to be changed multiplies loss and the probability of unintended consequences.

Beware of those who rip up the lawn to turn the garden over to grass.

It has become conventional wisdom to recognise that change is an inevitable fact of organisational life, that all things are changing all the time. In practice, this does not help and can even cause great, avoidable anxiety and confusion. At worst - and it frequently happens - essential services are unnecessarily disrupted, even destroyed, as change is bulldozed through, with complete insensitivity to what needs to be retained. This is far more likely when change managers focus on their innovation at the expense of all else.

We have found it helpful to recognise that things change at different rates, that relative to some rapidly changing dimensions of work and life, other things stay the same.

It should also be noted that many change strategies - wholesale restructuring, for example - often change things that, far from needing to change, actually need to be sustained.

It is common to find pockets of innovatory work which have pioneered new practice, destroyed when the new practice becomes general policy and implementation is attempted through re-structuring the organisation.

AT AN EARLY STAGE CHANGE MANAGERS NEED TO IDENTIFY:

- What needs to change?

  ✍

- What should and can stay the same?

  ✍

Outcomes and consequences: Changing the way that change is introduced

It is almost impossible to read and write about change and innovation, especially now that they are such buzz words in the management literature and the media, without implying a pro-change, pro-innovation bias. It may be assumed that to set out to 'manage' innovation is to assume that innovation is 'a good thing'. This is not so. It is clear that many innovations have disastrous consequences, either because they fail in significant elements, like the Titanic, or as a perverse result of their rampant success, like taking rabbits to Australia.

A major argument for improving our capacity to manage these processes is to reduce the harm that unplanned, uncontrolled, or mindless innovation can cause by identifying unintended consequences.

To be partially successful in introducing an innovation it is necessary, but not sufficient, to have the new idea in place, being used by those who are supposed to use it, and for it to have the intended impact.

To be successful the innovation has still to be relevant by the time that it is adopted and not causing or precipitating significant counter-productive, harmful, unintended consequences.

The successful management of innovation cannot be done by the management of objectives alone, it has to include active observation of, and response to, the consequences of change. This is not to say that the process of innovation can always be predicted or painless. We are aware that there is some truth in the old saying: 'you cannot make omelettes without breaking eggs'. But good cooks make sure they don't kill people with salmonella. They can also separate the white from the yokes as required, and if they want the shells it is easy enough to blow the eggs. It just takes knowledge and skill and a little time!

The community care reforms, like the development of many new products by industry, are as much attempts to undo past innovations as they are to address new problems or markets. A major force to change community care came from the escalating expenditure of social security budgets on residential care of elderly people. In addition to the original intentions, these payments began to be used to preserve social services departments' budgets for home based services and to expand private residential care, with the unintended consequence of increasing the number of people entering residential care against their wishes. We predict that current reforms of community care and the National Health Service, along with the Children Act, will also have perverse unintended consequences. One example will be the consequences of the introduction of care management to rationalise and increase the cost effectiveness of resource allocation. This innovation, devised in the USA to counter the fragmentation of service provision, could have the unintended consequences of splintering service provision, making service planning and monitoring more difficult, and introducing financial payments to replace 'informal' care arrangements.

Introducing a solution to a problem that does not exist is dangerous[1]. The 'solution' can contribute to the creation of the problem.

> The goal is not to implement a particular set of innovations

> It is to solve problems in the most effective way.

---

[1] Detaching a 'solution' or innovation from the problem it was designed to solve can have serious adverse consequences, but it could also be benificial. See the expanded discussion in *Managing Change Through Innovation (Smale, 1996)*.

CHAPTER SIX

Level Two: The Innovation Trinity.
Part 1 – The people

'We developed this new way of working despite the organisation; it was a struggle all the way'.

Energy is a vital ingredient in producing change. Many successful innovators are driven by their commitment to a new idea or vision of how services could be different. Such people achieve change using their capacity to sell a new idea, their natural ability to negotiate with, and to motivate people, and their 'nous': their political instincts. If they are in a senior position they back these attributes with their organisational authority, and are seen as effective leaders. More junior staff involved in 'bottom up' initiatives may feel that what they are doing is less legitimate, and other people's reactions to them may be more ambivalent. Either way, innovators often feel that they are working against forces of inertia, if not open hostility.

A planned approach to the management of change should increase the probability of change in the desired direction, improve on chance and reduce counter-productive consequences. Such an approach should help managers avoid inoculating the organisation against the innovation being introduced. Managers meeting resistance to change should assume that this is feedback to them on the way that they are managing the process. This may not be literally true, but they are not able to change the feelings, attitudes and motivations of others who are already hostile. They **are** able to modify their own behaviour which may influence others' feelings and behaviour in the future. If they change what they do they may increase the chances of success and reduce the negative consequences of the way that the change takes place.

Next steps

Having identified 'who sees what as a problem' and begun to promote a convergence in thinking about the appropriate solutions/innovations to be adopted, the change manager will move on to the next level of work, i.e. Level Two: planning through the innovation trinity, beginning with identifying the significant people.

Level Two: planning through the innovation trinity

Policy makers, senior managers or other agents of change, wishing to initiate practice development or introduce new methods of work, need to confront the three major dimensions of the innovation trinity:

- THE IDENTIFICATION OF THE SIGNIFICANT PEOPLE INVOLVED.

- THE ANALYSIS OF THE NATURE OF THE INNOVATION.

- UNDERSTANDING THE CONTEXT OF CHANGE.

Everett Rogers and his colleagues have brought together over three thousand studies on the diffusion of innovations, identifying many core characteristics of the people and the processes involved[2] (Rogers, 1983). They show how the progress of an innovation as it spreads through a social system can typically be shown on an S-shaped graph. The rate of adoption is described by the steepness of the curve.

Fig. I. The diffusion of innovations curve

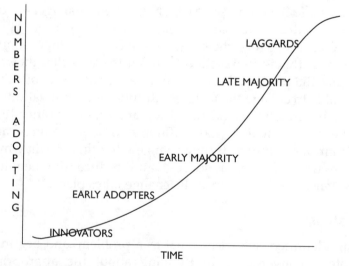

(Rogers, 1983 p.11)

---

[2] This number has now reached almost 4000 in the fourth edition of this work (Rogers, 1995).

We can see from this diagram that Rogers has indicated that there are different categories of people involved at each stage. He synthesises the research to identify the characteristics of the people in each category. We need to look at the *key players:* those people whose actions will determine whether an innovation is adopted. From this analysis the change agent will be able to identify what sort of action needs to be taken with whom, to plan the transactions that have to be undertaken to manage the adoption of the innovation.

The major players in the transfer of innovations

The research shows that there are significant categories of key players in addition to those identified on the graph, and that they display certain characteristics.

Innovators: The 'original' innovators are by definition the inventors, either researchers or practitioners who develop a new 'technology' which may be a form of service delivery or method of intervention. However, we have said that an innovation is a new machine, 'an idea, practice, or object that is perceived as new by an individual or another unit of adoption', and stressed the importance of recognising that an idea or practice does not have to be 'original' to be an innovation. The S-shaped curve (Fig. I) shows how an 'innovation' becomes less and less 'original' as it passes through time and up the curve, whilst still being an 'innovation' to the next group of people yet to adopt it. It follows from this definition that an '**innovator**' is somebody introducing an idea new to the recipients, which does not have to be 'original'.

Early adopters: Have been called 'venturesome'. They tend to be innovators themselves and actively seek information about new ideas. In many fields, from farming to medicine, they tend to differ from later adopters in having higher social status, more education and more favourable attitudes towards change and a greater ability to cope with uncertainty and risk. They tend to be part of a more highly interconnected social system, with their networks extending outside their own immediate professional and social circle, as well as having greater exposure to the mass media. Communication through the mass media about new ideas influences these early adopters. They are also persuaded by direct personal contact with innovators and other early adopters through visits and attendance at conferences and professional meetings.

Product champions: It is significant that in her research on innovation in the National Health Service, Stocking (1985) named 'Identifiable Enthusiasts' at the top of her list of factors influencing the rate of adoption of any innovation. Research evidence has some influence on early adopters, but it seems to play little part in the decisions of those in the 'majority' categories. 'Product champions' are crucial early adopters, being the people who not only adopt new methods, but take up the cause of spreading the message to others. Charles Handy (1981) has also stressed that managers wanting to introduce change should:

'Select an appropriate initiating person or group (appropriate in this context refers to sources of power as perceived by the recipients of the strategy)'.

As we have seen, the diffusion research makes it clear that the social and professional networks of product champions are crucial for spreading new ideas and methods.

Gatekeepers: Those who control the allocation or the distribution of resources. The Minnesota research programme included areas of innovation which involved large capital investment. In these circumstances the role of top management and investors as sponsors is crucial (Angle and Van de Ven, 1989). In social services area teams, the area director also often plays a significant role in providing, or at least legitimising the use of resources in a particular way.

However, there are many other gatekeepers of resources. Each person is to some extent the gatekeeper of their own resources of time and energy. Innovators in social work practice have often turned outside their organisation to develop resources when faced with little hope of increased finance from their agencies. Such development is as crucial to the implementation of the community care reforms as it is little recognised in much of the current discussions about care management. It is also the case that changes in practice can stall on the way that resources are released, or not, by relatively low-status administrators. These people can be effective gatekeepers. Using procedures which are frequently obsolete, they make it difficult for practitioners to acquire the resources senior managers have 'released'. These actions powerfully reinforce the would-be early adopter's sense of 'it can't be done here'.

> Remember, each worker is the gatekeeper of their own effort and other personal resources.

In addition to these research based categories, our development work has demonstrated the crucial significance of the following players:

Change agents: Those formally or informally employed to lead change, and those who develop and implement new methods of practice, management and organisation. This includes 'product champions' and could refer to:

- *process consultants*, 'outsiders' employed to help when an organisation or system gets stuck;
- *expert consultants*, employed when technical expertise needs to be imported to inform local staff about the innovations being adopted and the processes of development required;
- *transactors*, change agents using this approach to guide them through the transactions they need to undertake to manage change;

Consultants: This category overlaps with change agents. It is included to help identify those who formally or informally provide a 'sounding board' or 'professional supervision'. In essence, it is someone who can bring an informed third party perspective to the analysis, planning and interventions that make up the processes of planned change management. The main function of such a person is to enable the change agent to maintain their own 'marginal position' in the process and to help resist the natural tendency to get sucked into becoming a fixed part of the ongoing patterns of relationships.

> The people on the edge see the furthest.

Marginality is crucial so that the change agent can see other people's perspectives. The stance is central to implementing this, or any approach to managing change.

Marginality is positive, being marginalised by others is not. The key issue is who takes charge - or who takes the initiative and maintains the change agent's position as an outsider or as a person who has joined a social system without becoming a permanent, unthinking part of its processes.

Legitimate initiators: We have found that in some organisations it is not possible to introduce bottom up innovation without senior managers rejecting initiatives from those they feel should only respond to initiatives from the top. There are also some staff whose attitude to authority is such that they will reject initiatives because they come from the top. There are also situations where class, gender, cultural or ethnic differences make the acceptance of new ideas difficult. In all of these situations the initiating change agent will look for indigenous people who can legitimately introduce innovations in the eyes of those they want to adopt change

Minders: Many practitioners and managers who innovate within their organisations come into conflict with their peers and senior colleagues. Often those who are successful have 'a minder', someone in a senior management position who supports them when the going gets tough.

Angle and Van de Ven (1989) have pointed out that senior managers are often involved throughout the process and play four different roles: sponsor, critic, mentor, and institutional leader. The role of minder is compatible with these functions but has the specific dimension of protecting the innovator from others in the organisation, typically middle managers who try to stop the development of the innovation. We have already drawn attention to the tightrope early innovators walk between acceptable deviance and 'delinquency'. As Tom Peters of 'In Search of Excellence' fame says ' you can tell who the path finders are – they are the ones up ahead with the arrows in their backs'. The minder protects the innovator from those who would define innovation as delinquency and penalise the innovator. This leads us to the next category.

Opponents: Much of the literature gives the impression that the field contains active, positive people on the side of change, and those who are 'resistant' for a variety of reasons which have to be addressed by strategies for 'overcoming resistance to change'. In our experience, there are very few people happy with the status quo. There are those who, while advocating change, are hostile to the particular innovation under consideration. We suspect some so-called 'laggards' fall into this category. Such people resist the innovation because they are the product champions of an alternative innovation. Their existence is one of the reasons why it is necessary to go beyond the usual strategies of 'training' and 'restructuring' to develop an adequate approach to developing new methods of practice. There are also those who object to the way that change is being introduced.

Close collaborators: People you work with to introduce innovations and those with whom you can openly discuss analysis, strategies and tactics.

Network entrepreneurs: This final category of actor is of critical significance based on the central role performed by social networks as a medium for information and action. There is a tendency to talk of networks, be they diffusion networks, 'invisible colleges', 'natural helping networks', or neighbourhood relationships, as if they were totally spontaneous phenomena. In our experience networks are natural, even inevitable, but they do require energy to initiate and maintain them. We have called the people who work at linking people to others, those who initiate and maintain links between people and so 'make networks happen', 'network entrepreneurs'.

Key Players in the transfer of innovations: the people you now need to identify and add to your map.

Innovators: those who introduce an idea/method to new recipients - it does not have to be 'original'.

Change Agents: those formally or informally employed to implement innovation or to introduce new methods to others. This includes 'product champions' and could also refer to consultants (see below).

Product Champions: are crucial early adopters, being the people who not only adopt new methods, but take up the cause of spreading the message to others.

Early Adopters: have been called 'venturesome'. They tend to be innovators themselves and actively seek information about new ideas.

Later Adopters: are mainly influenced by local experience and by interpersonal contacts within a more restricted network of peers.

Laggards: are the most parochial people of the adopter groups and tend to take the past as their point of reference. **However, they are also often simply the last to be told!**

Opinion Leaders: those people within an organisation or profession who have an influence on the methods used by others.

Gatekeepers: those who control the allocation or the distribution of resources (including their own co-operation).

Consultants: informal or formal consultants - people who can provide a sounding board, or professional supervision. In essence, someone who can bring an informed third party perspective to the analysis, planning and interventions that make up the process of managed change.

Legitimate Initiators: a person who is seen by adopters as a legitimate person to be introducing change.

Minders: many practitioners and managers who innovate within their organisations come into conflict with their peers and senior colleagues. Often those who are successful have 'a minder', someone in a senior management position who supports them when the going gets tough.

Opponents: those who are hostile to the particular innovation under consideration, some 'resistant to change' and some so-called 'Laggards' fall into this category.

Close Collaborators: people change agents work with to introduce innovations and those with whom they can openly discuss analysis, strategies and tactics.

Network Entrepreneurs: the people who work at linking people to others, those who initiate and maintain links between people and so 'make networking happen'.

MAPPING II IDENTIFYING THE SIGNIFICANT PEOPLE

Revisit your map, identify all the key players. Add to your map by naming people who could fulfil all significant functions then:

Identify who has to do what.

What connections need to be made between people to mobilise the contagious process?

MAP II
(Remember ALL people are to some extent GATEKEEPERS of their own resources)

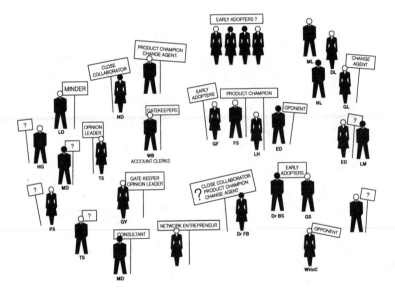

From identification to action

Beckhard and Pritchard (1992) suggest that the change agent should identify three major dimensions of each of the major actors:

'Do we need them to:
Make it happen;
Help it to happen, by providing resources;
Let it happen, by not blocking the process?'

(Beckhard and Pritchard, 1992 p.76)

We have found it helpful to expand on this and ask the following sets of questions:

WHO NEEDS TO MAKE IT HAPPEN AND TAKE ACTION FOR CHANGE:

- Bring product champions and the next adopters together?
  ✍

- Help it happen: release resources?
  ✍

- Support innovators and change agents?
  ✍

- Change their behaviour in their practice?
  ✍

- Change their behaviour so that their relationship with significant others changes?
  ✍

WHO HAS TO LET IT HAPPEN: KEEP OUT OF THE WAY:

- Who has to give their consent?
  ✍

- Who could sabotage the innovation?
  ✍

- Who has to not block resources?
  ✍

- Who has to refrain from diverting resources?
  ✍

- Who has to avoid taking counter-action?
  ✍

What does the innovation 'mean' to significant players?

People's reaction to change will depend on at least three major interrelated dimensions:

1. Are they ACTIVE or PASSIVE?

2. Does the Innovation CHANGE THEIR IDENTITY?

3. Do they perceive themselves as WINNING or LOSING?

1. Are they active or passive in the process: are they initiators or objects - even victims of change?

It cannot be stressed enough that adults learn through a *convergence* between what they already know and new ideas and knowledge. Where people stand in this process is crucial. A frequent exercise used in our innovation workshops and consultancy is to get people to place themselves in a line to represent a continuum from 'a person enthusiastically leading innovation' to 'a person having change imposed upon them'. Typically, the former are keen to learn all they can to further the cause of their innovation, while the latter have a marked tendency to exhibit the signs of learned helplessness. If they were simply rendered passive then they might be easier for the change manager to work with. In practice, many implicitly oppose change without declaring opposition but without demonstrating acceptance. Others will simply be obedient, agreeing with the changes and implementing all that they are told to do without using any initiative or adding personal commitment. At worst they will work to rule, at best they will simply do what they are told and delegate decision making and thinking upwards. Of course some innovations and some change managers require this kind of response.

> To have the rug pulled from under you is a very different experience from coming to a decision to reject the old flooring and choose a new carpet, or to move to another room.

> Those who only care if they have their hands on the rug and want to get the job done in the quickest possible way can expect to meet with great opposition, and take a long time to get through, or over it.

2. Does the innovation produce a change of identity?

The Luddites were not only being driven out of work: arguably more importantly, their skills and prestige as craftsmen were made obsolete. The history of technological change is littered with examples of the disastrous consequences of change agents who overlooked the significance of the meaning of the status quo for key participants and, intentionally or not, undermined their position. Technology is prone to these problems as smarter machines replace individual skill, machines that can be operated by less trained hands or no hands and minds at all. This is becoming clear to a new class of workers as IT machines take over educated, middle class jobs. But other innovations are more subtle in reframing, and in the eyes of some participants, degrading or upgrading their task.

Underestimating the meaning of innovations has caused particular problems when technology is transferred to different cultures where the meanings attributed to the same objects and actions will be very different. In the diffusion of innovations literature there are classic examples, such as the way that the introduction of steel axes undermined aboriginal culture in

Australia. The missionaries only saw the axe as a tool, while the aborigines saw the stone axe as a symbol of status and wisdom amongst the elders who were the only people who owned them. The differences in the cultures involved may be less obvious, such as the difference between 'management' and 'professional' cultures in many organisations. It is to be expected, for example, that home care organisers would see 'care management' as a promotion, while professionally qualified social workers who do not aspire to be 'managers' may see the same role as a dilution of their position.

The degree to which the task changes will of course determine the amount of learning and unlearning that staff have to do. Some staff will welcome the upgrading and reject the downgrading of tasks, just as others will want them to be easier. The change agent must recognise that it is what the change means for the individual that is crucial. Obviously few welcome less rewards from their work, and money is only one of the rewards people expect.

It should be stressed that it is the subjective experience of the people concerned that is of crucial significance. We have come across situations where managers intended to promote people, giving them more money and organisational authority, but have actually diminished the professional role and undermined the significance of the job as perceived by participants. Attempting to change occupational therapists into 'care managers' is one such example, that led to all the OTs leaving one authority despite increased pay and grading.

3. What do key people win or lose?

All change will involve a degree of loss and this will need to be taken into account. But the change manager needs to be able to distinguish between the expression of pain, which may be overcome or even transformed into positive experience if handled appropriately, and opposition, which escalates if managed badly.

As a first reaction, change managers would be wise to see resistance as negative feedback to their own interventions, and adapt their behaviour to increase support for the innovation. There are two main reasons for adopting this approach:

- change managers have more control over their own behaviour than they have over the attitudes and behaviour of others;

- they have limited time and space and it is probably best to assume that they should spend what is available building on strengths in the situation rather than focusing on the so-called 'pathology'.

Using the gardening metaphor again we could say that change managers should focus on fertilising growth without damage to the environment and mobilising the natural forces at our disposal. We do not immediately reach for the weed killer any more than we would introduce trees in pots to replace the ones we tore down in our haste to change the landscape.

People's so-called 'resistance' is often caused by their anticipated loss of identity through change. These losses are often compounded, and sometimes even caused, by the way change is mismanaged rather than as a response to the innovation itself. The good innovation manager will only be provoking unavoidable disruption, not making wholesale changes in the name of introducing new policies and practice. As we have seen from our discussion of innovation fallacies, reorganisation is often a good example of using a sledgehammer to crack a walnut; or, mixing metaphors, more like using a sledgehammer to re-mix the same cocktail!

Peter Marris (1974) has drawn attention to the significance of loss in all change processes, likening it to the grief of bereavement. This he describes as the expression of a profound conflict between contradictory impulses to consolidate all that is still valuable and important in the past and preserve it from loss, and at the same time to re-establish a meaningful pattern of relationships in which the loss is accepted. So in the management of change, we need to identify where a sense of bereavement is likely to be provoked. Winning for some is experienced as loss of the struggle by others. It is not just that there are winners and losers, but that all lose something and potentially gain something too. Kanter (1989), discussing the acute disruption involved in major reorganisations caused by corporate take-overs, warns managers that:

'Issue number one in managing a difficult transition smoothly is to allow employees to mourn the past, to grieve over their losses'.

To which she adds:

'The second key to commitment building during the restructuring process is getting the survivors excited about the future - offering positive vision to compensate for their loss'.

These considerations lead to our next two sets of plan building questions:

WHAT MEANING DOES THE STATUS QUO AND THE INNOVATION HAVE FOR ALL THE KEY PEOPLE INVOLVED?

Return to your maps to identify:

- For whom does the innovation change the purpose of the task?

- How does the innovation change the motivation of significant people?

  ✍

- Who will experience a change in status or image of themselves?

  ✍

- What symbolic significance is attached to the status quo by key players?

  ✍

- Who sees the innovation as what kind of symbol?

  ✍

WHAT IS THE IMPACT OF CHANGE ON INDIVIDUALS, WORKING GROUPS AND THE WIDER SOCIAL SYSTEM?

- Who experiences what as 'winning'?

  ✍

- Who experiences what as 'loss'?

  ✍

- How can you make sure that people have space to mourn their losses?

    ✍

- What can you do to build commitment to the new solutions and new situations?

    ✍

CHAPTER SEVEN

The Innovation Trinity.
Part II – Analysing the innovation

Different kinds of innovations require different management strategies and tactics depending upon the following dimensions:

1. How 'ADOPTABLE' they are:

How the innovation compares to the characteristics that affect the rate of adoption of a new idea or technology. Recognising this enables you to have realistic expectations about time, and so to set attainable deadlines.

2. The ORDER OF CHANGE in RELATIONSHIPS INVOLVED:

Whether there are changes within existing relationships or a change in the nature of the relationships between significant people. Understanding this enables you to see who needs to change what behaviour - crucial for identifying appropriate innovation management.

3. The STAGE THE INNOVATION IS AT in its own development.

Helps you to identify the action required to move from 'a good idea', to a new way of working or technology.

Dimension I: The characteristics of the easily adopted innovation

The attributes of innovations, like the attributes of adopters, contain a range of significant variables which affect the speed of adoption. Five major attributes affecting a wide range of innovations drawn from many fields of study have been identified (Rogers, 1983; Rogers and Kincaid, 1981):

- *Relative advantage:* the degree to which an innovation is perceived by the potential adopters as better than the idea it supersedes.

- *Compatibility:* the degree to which an innovation is perceived as consistent with the existing values, past experiences and needs of potential adopters.

- *Complexity:* the degree to which an innovation is perceived as relatively difficult to understand and use.

- *Trialability:* the degree to which an innovation may be experimented with on a limited basis.

- *Observability:* the degree to which the results of an innovation are visible to others.

Stocking's research on the diffusion of innovation within the NHS employed Roger's model, concluding that for an innovation to diffuse rapidly it will need to exhibit some or all of the following features:

- The existence of *identifiable enthusiasts:* those who invented or discovered the idea, who are keen to disseminate it, who have reasonable status in their profession or speciality groups, and who are prepared to put in considerable time and energy into promoting it. Everett Rogers names these people *'product champions'*.

- The innovation should *not be in conflict* with current national or organisational policies or established climates of opinion among professionals and other groupings.

- It needs to have *local appeal* to those who have the power to promote change.

- It has to *meet the perceived needs* of patients or of staff, must 'add-on' and not require major role or attitude changes, and be simple to organise.

- It should be *adaptable* to suit local circumstances.

- *Little finance or other resource is required* unless such requirements can be hidden, or increased resources be made available. (Stocking, 1985)

It has to be stressed that these are not the characteristics of 'good or relevant' innovations. They are simply those which 'diffuse rapidly'. They are then relatively easy for people to adopt, and so for change agents to introduce.

This analysis should help you to set realistic deadlines. If you have a complex innovation that many see as incompatible with their normal ways of working, it will take a long time to get all the significant people involved to change. You can, of course, rush through innovations and swallow the consequences of widespread opposition and all the problems provoked in people by enforced and unresolved loss. Time, and a different strategy, is involved when roles need to be re-negotiated. This leads to the analysis of the innovation and the order of change involved in relationships.

To identify how adoptable your innovation is, you will need to reflect on your map and ask:

HOW 'ADOPTABLE' IS THE INNOVATION?

How does the innovation compare to adoption criteria?

✍

Who perceives it as: a - better; b - no different; c - worse than the status quo?

✍

Who perceives it as: a - consistent; b - inconsistent; c - in conflict with local or national policies, with existing values?

✍

Who sees the innovation as complex?

✍

Can it be tried out before adoption?

✍

Can it be observed in operation elsewhere: where, and by whom?
✍

Does it require extra resources: if yes, what?
✍

Is it promoted by identifiable enthusiasts: who are they or who could become them?
✍

Dimension II: Orders of change, a change within the rules or a change in the rules?

The analysis of the type of change *in the relationships involved in the innovation* has proved to be one of the most important dimensions of managing change and innovation. It is of particular relevance to empowerment issues, the devolution of resource management, working in partnership with service users, and collaboration between professionals and agencies.

Most writers on the management of change make a distinction between different orders of change: radical or routine; revolutionary or evolutionary; fundamental or incremental.

A useful way of understanding such changes is to see them as 'first order' and 'second order' change in the relationships between people.[3]

A first order change is a change within the rules of a given system: within the existing pattern of relationships between people even where tasks change significantly. First order change takes place without change in the existing role relationships between people.

---

[3] This distinction was made by Watzlawick and colleagues (1974) applying communication theory to change in human systems.

A change in procedures, introducing training in multi-culturalism, shifting resources around within existing programmes, decentralising a main office: all would fall under the description of a first order change where the existing pattern of relationships remains in place. Managers introducing first order change can often alter what they say should be done and not change what they do themselves. In first order changes, the task, and how it is done, may change in major ways, but the way that people relate to each other does not. The impact of giving a word processor to a secretary is of this order, on the relationship between secretary and manager. Work can be done in a radically different way but the relationship between these two people stays the same.

Second order change occurs when there is a change in the rules, a change in the nature of the system, when rules and the boundaries of a system of relationships change in an unprecedented way, when patterns of relationship are altered. The roles of each party in relationships change.

To promote workers' discretion and judgement in lieu of prescribed procedure, to undertake an analysis and redress of institutional racism, to change the process for allocating resources, to devolve decision making: all will involve second order changes in significant relationships.

Managers initiating second order change have to alter what they do when they are an integral part of the relationships being affected by change.

In relationships undergoing second order changes the task and/or methods change and so does the nature of the relationship between people. If a manager starts using a lap-top computer, it is likely not only to change the way that work gets done: it also radically affects the relationship between secretary and manager.

Different action has to be taken to manage these different orders of change. To introduce first order changes the manager may carry on behaving in the same way while changing what she expects to be done. To introduce a second order change in relations, to change the rules, the manager will have to change her own behaviour in the relationships that have to change.

Introducing second order changes as if they were first, leads to great confusion and often hostility or paralysis. Consider what happens when a manager, who typically relates to staff by issuing instructions, wants to get staff to make decisions themselves and does this by continuing to tell them what to do. This will lead to the manager ordering people to take the initiative. But, by definition, people can only take the initiative themselves. To behave in this way and to say what he does, the manager places staff in a 'be spontaneous' double bind: 'I order you not to need orders'.

Another example is to tell your children that they have responsibility for spending their own pocket money, and then subsequently tell them what they should and should not spend it on. Your behaviour contradicts the message; you communicate two things at once. Should they do what you say or do what fits in with your behaviour? When this happens everyone will be upset, except those who fail to hear or notice one of the messages. Contradictory verbal messages are confusing enough, but double binds come about when actions and words contradict each other, and are particularly damaging. Staff will often reject one or both communications because of the contradictions in messages, even when they agree with one, or even both of them: 'I want to do it, but resent being told what to do by you'.

> First order changes involve renegotiating tasks and methods. Second order changes involve renegotiating tasks, methods and roles and relationships.

It probably means changing the way that negotiations take place so that they are carried out in a way that begins to put the new relationships into practice. A plan for devolved decision making should be arrived at jointly. A plan drawn up at the top and handed down for consultation enters into the world of paradox where the mode of communication contradicts the message.

It is vital to distinguish between first and second order change to ensure that the **way** that an innovation is being introduced does not undermine the innovation itself. This will be crucial for those implementing the current reforms in health and social policy, particularly where the management intention is to fundamentally change the nature of the relationships between the public and those who serve them. Can staff involve 'patients' and 'service users' as partners in decision making if these same managers continue to retain the right to remake the decisions and thus effectively undo the decisions made in partnership with others?

These issues, like many in this book are discussed further in *Managing Change Through Innovation (Smale, 1996)*. The expanded discussion looks at how different change agent approaches are needed to tackle changes in the basic assumptions upon which work is based as well as changing patterns of behaviour.

This leads to the third phase of mapping.

MAPPING III

Return to your maps and identify the order of change in crucial relationships:

1. Within which relationships is the innovation a first order change: a change within the rules that govern the relationship. In first order changes the task, and how it is done, changes but the way people relate to each other fundamentally stays the same.

2. Within which relationships does the innovation involve a second order change: a change in the rules that govern the relationship between people, where the task changes and so does the nature of the relationship between people?

Which in turn raises key questions for change managers:

How do you need to change your behaviour to change the relationships you have with significant people?
✍

Within which relationships do you need to initiate a renegotiation of the way in which key players relate to each other: a renegotiation of their reciprocal roles?
✍

Dimension III: Innovation and time

The Minnesota research programme (Van De Ven et al, 1989) examined the development stages of innovations within a variety of kinds of organisations, from large commercial and industrial companies to new firms and public service organisations. They focused on the 'initiation', the 'development' and the 'implementation/termination' periods of an innovation's development.

The initiation period

Although the romantic picture is of new ideas coming like a flash of light, such as Archimedes' experience in the bath or Newton's collision with the apple, the evidence is that it takes much longer to work out how to apply them. [4] Most innovations are not initiated in a short space of time. They have long gestation periods, often lasting several years, during which coincidental events occur that 'set the stage' for the introduction of the innovation. Darwin's years of consideration of the origin of the species seems more typical than Newton's apple.

However, it is the case that crises, or 'shocks' trigger concentrated efforts to progress an innovation. (Darwin published when it became apparent that a rival was near to producing a similar theory.) These shocks may come from internal or external sources to the organisation. Often they are caused by people reaching a threshold of dissatisfaction with existing conditions. Innovation is the action taken to resolve the dissatisfaction. These findings have much in common with explanations of change to be found in catastrophe theory; the underlying theory of crisis intervention; and the development of new paradigms in the development of scientific theories. In all of these theories there is the combination of the right circumstances for a change to take place and the coming together, or collision of previously unconnected ideas or entities.

The initiation period requires time for interested staff to come together to sort out ideas and to turn them into new approaches to practice. The implementation of policy changes from the top also requires such time if staff are to work out how change is going to be implemented by them. This is the time required to

---

[4] Managers may like to note that, like many major solutions to persistant problems, neither of these ideas came from rushing about, but from lying down and thinking!

engage with staff to begin the work that we have described here as Level One activity.

The developmental period

> To bring about changes in practice there can be no substitute for persistent effort over time.

This is true for changing either management behaviour or the actions of staff on the front line. It takes at least four years for the motor car industry to develop a new model, from market testing on to concept design through prototype building and many other development phases, to tooling up the lines and finally selling and producing the new model. Many commercial organisations spend huge sums on the development phases of research and development. All too often in public services it is assumed that research can be disseminated in a raw form and turned into new practices by front line managers and staff. It is as if we believed that all you need to do is present the latest ideas in car design to the shop floor management and workers and let them get on with developing and building the new cars.

The processes involved in the development phase of innovations are rarely straightforward. Typically, once a developmental process has begun, the original innovation quickly proliferates into several ideas. This makes the path of the innovatory process complex to manage. Managers should anticipate difficulties in maintaining the continuity of organisational learning from the development of new practices. Research carried out in many organisations highlights several key staffing issues. Normal staff turnover is a major factor as an innovation takes shape. Typically people were not involved in full time development work on a particular innovation, so commitment varied with other work pressures rather than the demands of the innovation and change management. Moreover, technically competent staff are often working at the edge of their capacity because the nature of the innovation process means that they have little or no experience of the work at hand. These factors increase instability. Although people often work best under such conditions, the organisation can find itself more dependent upon key staff who hold most of the unfolding knowledge of both the new product or approach, and the process of change in their heads.

Managers should also anticipate having to manage changing feelings throughout the innovation and change processes.

Innovation participants often experience intense excitement during the initiation of innovation, frustration and pain in the middle period as they work out the details of implementation and work with all the key people involved, and loss of a long held goal at the end of the innovation journey.

Changing human emotions represent some of the most difficult problems for those leading innovation and change. Managers will have to manage these feelings as well as those of staff 'on the receiving end' of change if they are not to become destructive forces in the organisation.

Full implementation and/or termination periods

We have stated that a crucial dimension of managing change is to distinguish between what stays the same and what needs to change. Research indicates that throughout the developmental period 'home grown' innovations are usually implemented by linking and integrating the 'new' with the 'old,' as opposed to substituting, transforming, or replacing the old with the new.

In large centralised organisations a crucial role is played by top management where there is a need for them to be committed to the development of an innovation. In the health and social services fields the support of managers, especially when they are gatekeepers of resources, has also been shown to be important for the development of some innovations. But many innovations, and probably most practice developments, also take place 'despite the organisation'. Peters and Waterman (1982) reflect on the same processes in the commercial and industrial world and emphasise the need for managers to take this into account and to give their staff room to 'bootleg', that is to take time out to develop ideas for new products alongside the performance of their normal tasks. The management literature increasingly highlights the success of the companies, such as 3M, who encourage this kind of activity.

To consider the stage that the innovation is at, and so the further development activity required, change managers will need to consider the following questions:

AT WHAT STAGE IS THE INNOVATION IN ITS OWN DEVELOPMENT:

- Initiation: What activities need to be. undertaken to turn good ideas into practical proposals for implementation?

  ✍

- Development: What action needs to be undertaken to adapt innovations to the particular circumstances pertaining in specific adoption sites?

  ✍

- Implementation: The process of developing an innovation, or major changes involving a series of innovations can be planned using the workbook presented here.

  ✍

CHAPTER EIGHT

The Innovation Trinity.
Part III. Understanding the context

Understanding the context within which you are trying to bring about change begins by understanding which way the wind is blowing and what is blowing in the wind. What other changes are already taking place in the organisation and the communities and markets it serves? What changes in policy have, or are likely to take place? What are the changing needs of service users and customers and how do they perceive their future needs? We need to understand these forces if we are to use them to help get to where we want to go.

A metaphor that is commonly used to describe the process of managing change is to liken the manager struggling with all the different factors to a juggler who has to keep all the balls in the air while standing on a moving platform.

Movement in the platform is introduced to the metaphor to add a level of complexity which illustrates that this precarious exercise is even more difficult than on first sight because of the ever changing nature of the world in which the manager lives.

This view of management is not only difficult to live up to, it is potentially dangerous. An approach to change which emphasises the difficulties in this way is also misleading. It is not helpful to try to live up to the picture of the metaphor and try to keep control of all aspects of the problem all the time. The trick is to distinguish between what changes and what stays the same, to be specific about the innovation and to understand the environment within which it is taking place. Managers cannot control everything all the time; they can, however, nudge events in the direction they want them to go if they intervene successfully.

We can illustrate a more realistic approach by looking further into the metaphor. Good jugglers drop balls all the time as they push back the frontiers of their skill (although they may choose not to practice new moves in public). An essential part of a jugglers act is to have a repertoire of 'recoveries', trick ways of picking up dropped balls that add to the perceived skill of the act.

Putting the juggler on a moving platform does not change his relationship to the balls: it does not make juggling more difficult. True, he may have to take some air resistance into account, but the balls will move through the environment at the same speed as the juggler. If the platform was moving at the same speed and in the same direction as a prevailing wind, it would make juggling much easier. If the wind was very strong, it may be that the only way a juggler could perform on that day is to be placed on a platform moving at the same speed and in the same direction as the wind.

So it is with the management of innovation. We have stressed that it is useful to break down global notions of 'change' into separate innovations, to differentiate between types of innovation within a package of reforms and to look at what does and what does not change. Systems theory, as referred to in the discussion of first and second order change, draws attention to the way in which reciprocal patterns of behaviour can become stuck, perpetuating the status quo and making change difficult. An analysis of these patterns can lead to interventions designed to change the rules and to release participants so that they can move on to new behaviour. But it does not always help to draw attention to the possibility that any change will have infinite repercussions and so change everything. Such pictures can conjure up paralysis in the most ambitious change agent. As we see with the juggler metaphor the relationship between the elements, their movement relative to each other, is crucial. Again we see the need to differentiate between the elements in a sea of change.

Time is the key issue. It is true that all is flux and that everything is changing. But just as it is often useful to act as if the earth is flat even though it is actually round, so it is helpful to recognise that some things stay the same relative to others, even though everything is constantly changing. This 'illusion' of stability may be necessary for our sanity; it certainly helps to understand the relative relationships between the various changes that are taking place when intervening to introduce an innovation.

The change manager needs to look at the other changes in the environment to see 'which way the wind is blowing', looking for the compatibility of the innovation with already-accepted changes, to be able to link the innovation to movements that are already going in the same direction. Just as the change manager will be identifying the key players to seek allies, so she will be looking at what else is changing and will seek support from the nature of compatible movements. Management writers stress the need to promote synergy within organisations; that is the parallel development of compatible elements that provide benefits above and beyond what units can do separately.

Our approach to managing innovations is not to focus on 'overcoming resistance' to change but to seek out those people and movements that are moving in the same direction. The skill of negotiation is in being able to find a 'win win' situation where all parties can be satisfied enough with what they get from a deal. Where this cannot be achieved we suggest that it is always better to adopt a judo approach to confrontation with those who want practice to develop in a different way; that is to turn your opponent's impetus to your own advantage rather than to try to meet force with force.

The motivation behind other changes and the force of organisational authority will be important just as the strength of the wind is important to sailors. Variable and gusty winds require constant responses from a sailor, just as change agents need to be agile in their management of change to make best use of changes in the context they work in.

Key questions for further developing the change management plan include:

UNDERSTANDING THE CONTEXT: WHICH WAY IS THE WIND BLOWING?

- What is going on which is compatible with the innovation?
  ✎

- What changes are going in a different direction?
  ✎

- What other changes can the innovation be linked to, to gain support?
  ✎

- Are other organisations involved open to such innovation?
  ✎

- Is the innovation compatible with the prevailing cultures?
  ✍

The change manager will also have to address questions about the organisation which help or hinder the progress of the innovation.

It is important to recognise that innovation, like crisis, highlights the flaws in the organisation's structure and management in the way that antifreeze finds leaks in a water cooling system. Problems arise, such as confusion over who makes what decisions, and unclear lines of accountability. It is not uncommon to work with would-be change managers who do not know, and cannot discover who has to give permission for a particular innovation to proceed.

A major issue confronting the change manager is what to do about these flaws: whether to engage in remedial activity to change the organisation, or find a way round these problems to progress the innovation despite the organisation. The scope of their responsibility will be a crucial factor in the decision. Many of the successfully innovatory practitioners and managers that we have worked with over the years have introduced new ways of working despite their own organisation. Others have got stuck into, and often stuck in the quagmire of their organisation's pathology.[5]

The next step in managing change involves returning to your maps and seeking the answers to the next set of questions.

MAPPING IV

Add to the map key dimensions of your analysis of the wider context, noting the people involved in making the different winds blow.

---

[5] Many of the characteristics of innovative organisations are those of innovative individuals, with some significant differences. See: **Managing Change Through Innovation** (Smale, 1996).

The next questions:

UNDERSTANDING THE CONTEXT

Are the required resources available?

- *Time:* Unrealistic deadlines erode the expertise of those involved, indicate management ignorance of the task, undermine the credibility of the innovation and often contradict the original intentions of change.
  ✍

- *People:* Are there significant gaps in the 'who has to do what' map?
  ✍

- Are other resources available?
  ✍

- How can missing resources be made available? (revisit gatekeepers and others?)
  ✍

CHAPTER NINE

Level Three: Negotiation, Staff and Organisation Development

Those engaged in adopting new methods of work often need to acquire new knowledge and skills. The need to identify the training implications of new policy initiatives is widely recognised. But training individuals is only one part of changing people's practice. There are important functions that have to be carried out by managers as they literally 'manage' the process of change. If new skills are not to be quickly eroded by attempts to fit them into old customs and practices, the organisation has to change to assist managers and practitioners implementing new methods.

The medium and the message

> The transfer of new forms of practice is a contagious process. Change managers need to introduce 'virulent viruses' into organisations to spread new practice

It is important to address the relationship between the mode and content of staff and agency development, whether initiated by agency managers or external change agents.

> The way an innovation is disseminated should be governed by the nature of the proposed new method of practice.

Change managers and staff developers need to be able to practise what they preach. Beside the obvious reasons of integrity, there are more pragmatic reasons. It has long been recognised that 'leadership by example' is the best, and often necessary dimension of management. A crucial element in the spread of new methods is access to adequate 'role models': people who deliberately or unintentionally can demonstrate how a new method of practice is done.

Most people adopt a new method of practice by copying peers, opinion leaders or 'product champions', a process of contagion rather than conversion. Those setting out to introduce a new method, be they managers, trainers or some other kind of change agent, will inevitably be seen as a model. Intentionally or not, those we seek to influence are far more likely to 'do what we do' rather than 'do what we say they should do'. The absence of an adequate supply of such people is one, if not the major reason why new approaches to practice can be so fervently advocated by all, but not applied in practice. Another is the lack of opportunities for learning through 'coaching', where new skills can be developed and new knowledge applied by supervised practice over time. Skill cannot be developed just by reading the training manual. Skilled coaching over time is required to develop new habits and to apply new knowledge.

We are not always aware of many of the ideas and behaviours that make up skilled practice or experienced management. Most professional behaviour involves a tacit understanding of what is involved, conscious knowledge being the tip of the iceberg. Coaching, a system of observing and giving direct feedback on behaviour, is required to identify and change the tacit understanding we have of our practice.

'Training' or renegotiation of roles and relationships?

Any discussion of the 'training implications of new policy' should first question whether 'training' or staff development is the right activity.

> Where the introduction of an innovation means a change in the roles and relationship of staff, then these new relationships need to be renegotiated. Where the innovation changes the nature of the task and/or conditions of service then negotiation between management and staff also precedes staff development and training.

'Training' as a way of getting staff or colleagues to accept 'management policy' has become commonplace in many organisations. There is a danger that this approach suffers from the problems described in Chapter 6: a 'second order change' being introduced as if it were a 'first order change'.

It is more effective, and arguably more honest, for managers to negotiate changes in relationships, tasks and service conditions rather than attempt to manage change through 'training events'. For example, 'training' nurses and social workers in each other's 'roles and functions' is put forward as a way of achieving collaboration. It will be more effective to recognise that role relationships have to be negotiated by both sides. An alternative to 'training' is to get nurses and social workers together to negotiate who can best do what at a local level and how they can communicate to achieve their separate and joint goals.

This leads us to return to your maps to identify:

LEVEL THREE: NEGOTIATIONS

Who has to carry out what negotiations with whom to get agreement for changes in working practices and changes in significant relationships?

✍

Choosing an appropriate approach to staff and organisation development

Having negotiated changed roles and practices, and identified staff development needs, change managers will need to choose the appropriate mode of staff development to fit the needs of staff and the proposed changes in practices.

FIVE MODES OF STAFF AND ORGANISATION DEVELOPMENT

1. Consciousness raising events

2. Training courses in specific skills, or aspects of service delivery

3. Workshops on team building

4. Workshops on interdisciplinary working

5. Reorganisation and development of inter group relationships

1. Consciousness raising events

These include conferences which present and illustrate the major dimensions of a new approach to practice, new policy initiatives or major research findings. The major advantages of an innovation and its achievements as demonstrated by early evaluations can be communicated to a wide variety of audiences. The uninitiated or the uninvolved can be informed of what the choices are. These events complement, and introduce people to literature about practice experience and research. They are only the very first step in the spread of a new method, promoting knowledge about what could be done. They put ideas into the heads of those who want to hear and think about them.

Diffusion of innovations research indicates that these events influence other innovators and 'early adopters' and have little impact on others. They are important for informing 'product champions' and giving them the opportunity to compare notes. These events should be targeted at these people and the 'opinion leaders' in the area of concern. They cannot be expected to change practice on their own nor can it be expected that participants will go back to their agencies and bring about change without engaging in more change management strategies.

Consciousness raising events also include exchanges between experienced innovatory practitioners and managers. There is a need for information and sharing of ideas amongst the initiated. This helps them develop the conceptual and theoretical base for new developments and the technology of new practice and approaches to management. 'Product champions' are more likely to want to attend such gatherings and gain considerably from such activities.

2. Training events

This includes the short course and skills workshop format of a few days' length, extending up to longer-term training packages, through the spectrum to post qualifying courses leading to higher level qualifications. These events can be targeted at particular areas:

(a) *Specific skills and knowledge areas*: particular staff groups frequently need to develop skills and knowledge in specific areas to implement innovation.

(b) *Innovatory aspects of service*: knowledge and experience of innovators needs to be passed on to individual workers and implemented in their teams.

3. Workshops on team building

> A 'team' is a group of people whose combined efforts are required to complete the whole of a task.

There are many reasons why workers need to work effectively together, particularly where the tasks undertaken involve a series of people. Collaborative approaches to social services delivery and practice embrace the functions of the whole agency and partnerships with health and other professionals, other agencies and organisations, and members of the public. Any one manager or member of staff should be expected to be in several, or many teams. Although we typically focus staff development on individuals, 'teamworking' is crucial to changing practice.

Specialisation and the division of labour requires a high degree of collaborative working to make the best collective impact. Training individuals may equip them to carry out their own tasks but it is insufficient where collaborative working should be the norm. It is necessary to look explicitly at how people are relating to each other as one part of team building. But for many, *team building* will be focused on their shared tasks. Teams, however constituted, have to work together on how they are going to identify their goals and tasks, draw up priorities consistent with agency policy, divide their effort and relate to each other so that their customers and more distant colleagues do not experience their 'help' as a chronic series of well-meaning beginnings with different people. They should also jointly monitor the impact of their efforts.

4. Workshops on inter-disciplinary working

The way in which boundaries are drawn around a 'team' may be idiosyncratic and is often a legacy of history rather than based on a rational definition of who is needed to carry out joint tasks. Are home care workers in or out of social services area teams? Should social workers be in primary health care teams, or health visitors in community care teams? The answers to these questions should depend upon the nature of the key tasks and methods adopted to achieve them given local circumstances and other community and agency resources. Increasingly there is a recognition of the importance of inter-agency groupings: 'virtual organisations'. There can then be no clear distinction between 'team building' and 'inter-disciplinary working'.

All the arguments put forward for team development similarly apply to inter-agency and inter-disciplinary working. Different staff have to negotiate who should do what with whom, based on the actual levels of skill, knowledge and resources that exist at the local level, rather than formalised distinctions or stereotyped pictures of what each other can or should contribute. A review of the development needs of staff in health and social services who adopted a community orientated approach, stressed that there are at least three parties to any effective partnership: one or more professionals, service users and their carers (Domoney, Smale and Warwick, 1989). People can be prepared by orthodox training, but it is much more likely, in our experience, that practice will be changed when development work takes place within and between agencies and directly involves patients and service users.

5. Reorganisation and the development of inter-group relations

Task-led organisations, those sensitive to their public, will be constantly evolving to meet constantly changing needs. The model that people have of organisations is crucial for understanding these processes. Seeing organisations as machines to be taken apart and rebuilt as if they were inanimate collections of objects is increasingly obsolete in the management literature, even if it lives on in the minds and actions of many managers and policy makers. Other models or metaphors will invite managers and policy makers to see this differently. A human systems approach, for example, will invite people to see their actions as attempting to change the patterns of reciprocal behaviour, or the 'culture' of the organisation.

Change managers need to recognise that as practice changes so elements of the organisation will need to change, and the relationships between different groups will be affected by first and second order changes in parallel with such changes in individual relationships. Change agent organisations will need to change as they are successful in changing the problems they set up to tackle. Planned obsolescence should be the goal of any such organisation.

These considerations will lead you to return to your MAPS to identify the following three areas of Level Three activity:

WHO NEEDS TO PARTICIPATE IN:

- Consciousness raising events?

  ✍

- Conferences and forum discussions illustrating the major dimensions of a new approach to practice, service delivery and policy initiatives?

  ✍

- Experienced practitioner/manager forums for information exchange amongst the initiated, to develop new practice?

  ✍

WHO NEEDS WHAT FORM OF STAFF DEVELOPMENT?

- Staff development programmes on specific skills, professional and personal development, or aspects of service delivery?

  ✍

- Who needs what knowledge?

  ✍

- Who needs to develop which skills?
  ✍

- Who will need coaching over time?
  ✍

- Who will be affected by a change in relationships?
  ✍

- Whose jobs will be changing?
  ✍

- Who will need counselling and support?
  ✍

WHAT RE-ORGANISATION AND INTER-GROUP DEVELOPMENT ACTIVITIES NEED TO TAKE PLACE?

- Workshops on team building?
  ✍

- Workshops on interdisciplinary working?
  ✍

- Who needs to do *what* with *whom* about:

Physical issues (e.g. space, geographical location)?

✍

Personnel?

✍

Finance?

✍

Quality and standards?

✍

Administration?

✍

Liaison?

✍

Monitoring?

✍

CHAPTER TEN

Level Four: Feedback, Management by Consequences and Further Action

From taking the first steps in discovering who sees what as a problem through to discussing people's training needs, the change manager will be picking up feedback from people about their reaction to the proposed changes and the way that its introduction is being managed. It is important to recognise that 'feedback' comes from all forms of communication: from verbal responses, to people's behaviour. Caution is always required about interpreting the motivations behind behaviour and open discussion is to be encouraged wherever possible. Remember the process of adopting new ideas is one of convergence, a synthesis of the current with the new. The chances of success in managing change will often depend upon promoting convergence and minimising divergence and this is difficult when communication is not open and frank. All change means stepping into the unknown, and trust in change agents is a key dimension to success and, again, dependent upon open negotiations and communication.

To help identify all feedback, return to your maps and talk to key people directly and indirectly involved. Listen to and look for all feedback (behaviour and words).

IDENTIFY:

- From whom are you getting positive feedback?
  ✍

- From whom are you getting negative feedback?
  ✍

- Who is reacting positively or negatively to the innovation itself?

  ✍

- Who is reacting positively or negatively to the way that the innovation is being introduced: change is being managed?

  ✍

Do more of what works - less of what provokes hostility.

Work with allies - do not put all of your energy into 'Overcoming resistance'.

'Resistance' and 'hostility' are negative feedback: change the way that the innovations are being introduced or change the innovation.

Manage by identifying consequences, not by objectives alone.

Beware the assumption that 'successful implementation' will be 'good'.

Do not just focus on the adoption of an innovation.

All changes should be judged by their impact on all those that they affect and not simply by whether they happen or not.

ASK:

- Does the innovation still address the problems it is supposed to?

  ✍

- What consequences does the innovation have beyond those intended?

  ✍

We have already indicated that the bottom line is not to be found in simply getting an innovation adopted, be it the implementation of policy changes or the development of new practice. The key issues are: does it solve the problems that it sets out to solve, does it precipitate unwanted consequences and is it still relevant to current circumstances.

All actions have a range of consequences, some desirable, some undesirable. Undesirable consequences, such as pollution following new industrial processes, have to be tackled with new innovations in their turn. Not all unintended consequences are bad. 'Windfall profits' from a new product being used in ways not imagined by inventors are common. Many major innovations are by-products of the intended invention. Examples include the many inventions of the alchemists even though they failed to make gold. What is important for the change manager is that they evaluate what actually happens as a result of their interventions, and not just the narrow area of goal achievement. There are a range of different consequences to look out for:

Different consequences

Desirable – – – – – – – – – – – – – – – – – – undesirable

Anticipated – – – – – – – – – – – – – – – – – unanticipated

Direct – – – – – – – – – – – – – – – – – indirect

You will see that undesirable, unanticipated and indirect consequences tend to go together just as do their opposites. Change mangers should be warned that it is often not possible to separate the desirable from the undesirable consequences: the advantages of nuclear power come with the risks.

New industrial technologies are no longer judged simply on their effectiveness and efficiency. Their impact on the environment has also to be taken into consideration. The management of change and innovation should be a reflective and a self reflective process: it should include monitoring the impact of the innovation on people; and also monitoring the consequences of the management process itself. If a method does not work an innovation is called for to replace it. If the innovation does not have all the desired consequences then it will need to be reinvented, or replaced in its turn by a new innovation.

If the way in which changes are introduced has undesirable consequences that too has to be replaced by a different way of introducing innovations.

When unanticipated people prove to be in the path of change unintended consequences often arise. It has been suggested that the maps drawn in the early stages of change management should, like medieval maps, have spaces marked: here lie dragons.[5]

Monitor the adoption and adaptation of the innovation in terms of its effectiveness as a response to the original problem, not just in terms of how well it is adopted: its 'adoption success':

This leads us to return to our maps and address the penultimate set of questions:

---

[5] MacLellan, M., Personal Communication.

MAPPING V

Identify what the consequences of change are for all the people on the map

Add to the map those who are caught up in the consequences of change and not previously identified

- Does the innovation solve the original problem?
  ✍

- Are the original intentions still relevant?
  ✍

- Identify unintended consequences - direct and indirect.
  ✍

If there are undesirable, unintended consequences, change the way that change is being managed or change the innovation or both.

CHAPTER ELEVEN

Finally, Start Again

'Well at least it passed the time'

'It would have passed anyway'

('Waiting for Godot')

By this time much will have happened. Your maps will be changing as people leave and join, as well as through your own discoveries. The innovation will have been reshaped and adapted, in as much as you and others have been able to fit it to your human environment and change the environment to accommodate it. Now it is time to ask the final set, or, is it the first set of questions:

- **How are today's problems best solved?**

- **How are your goals achieved?**

- **For whom is the new status quo a problem?**

- **Who wants change and for what reason?**

Final summary

This approach to introducing new forms of practice and managing change can be summarised in the following diagram. The different overlapping levels of activity are represented by interlocking triangles (the triangle is a symbol for change).

Fig 2

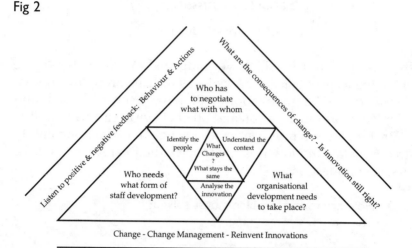

Change - Change Management - Reinvent Innovations

LEVEL ONE: Laying the Foundations for Change

This fundamental level of work looks at: identifying the changes to be introduced and the component innovations; considering the relationship between the proposed innovations and the problems they attempt to address. Change managers work out *what needs to change* and *what should stay the same* by asking *'For Whom is the Status Quo a Problem'* and *'Who Sees the Innovation as a Solution'*. We all know that everything changes over time, but this awareness does not help in practice. The change agent needs to understand the relative rate of change. To be more precise we could say: identify 'What Needs to Change relative to What Should Stay the Same'.

The three triangles round the centre describe the Second Level of activity:

LEVEL TWO: The Innovation Trinity

This is the core of the approach. It looks at how change managers can plan change by:

- *MAPPING THE PEOPLE: to identify all the key players*

- *ANALYSING THE INNOVATION: to plan appropriate action and time-scales*

- *UNDERSTANDING THE CONTEXT: to use it to your advantage.*

The three outer triangles describe:

LEVEL THREE: Negotiation, Staff and Organisation Development

Working at this level will help you to identify the negotiations that need to take place and who needs what form of staff training and what organisational development should take place.

Finally, the outer border of the triangle contains the key dimensions of:

LEVEL FOUR: Feedback, Consequences and Changing Change Management

In the introduction we stressed that this is not a step by step model and that managers and practitioners using this approach will not complete level one and then proceed neatly on to level two. There is a logic to such a sequence, but 'real life' is often much more complex than such elegant logic.

In this final chapter we have said that at the end of the process of implementing, or more precisely reinventing the innovations, or even long before this time, the change agent will need to start the process again. The triangles summarise all the activities but perhaps give too neat and too mechanistic a picture of the processes. In practice, the processes look much more like fig 3 as action at each level causes the change agent to return to other levels of activity. For example, discovering new key players will mean that the change agent has to reconsider who sees what as a problem. These overlapping activities will be returned to, not as change agents 'go back to the beginning', but as they return to basic questions as they spiral through time.

Fig 3

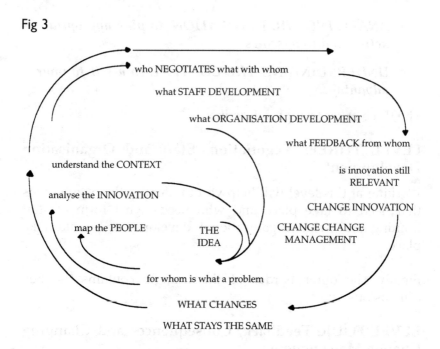

who NEGOTIATES what with whom

what STAFF DEVELOPMENT

what ORGANISATION DEVELOPMENT

what FEEDBACK from whom

understand the CONTEXT

is innovation still RELEVANT

analyse the INNOVATION

CHANGE INNOVATION

map the PEOPLE

THE IDEA

CHANGE CHANGE MANAGEMENT

for whom is what a problem

WHAT CHANGES

WHAT STAYS THE SAME

CHAPTER TWELVE

Epilogue

This Chapter reflects on the important questions: what to change, and where to look for the best innovations? It suggests that the real challenge facing change managers is that we may need to go backwards as well as forwards to make real progress rather than just promote change.

We started this work with a pro-innovation bias. Our goal was to develop an approach that helped change managers achieve their task, not to suggest what should or should not be changed. We have, however, learnt to warn against a pro-innovation bias. We are constantly reminded of the crucial importance of the basic questions: *what changes* and *what stays the same?*

We have come across many examples of good practice dismantled by accident. This may seem strange, even incomprehensible to the outsider. Inside large organisations, however, it is common enough. We have stressed that any change is likely to provoke unintended and unwanted consequences. Managers struggling with major reorganisations are bound to precipitate such consequences. They are often so busy with the next round of change that they do not see the impact of their previous actions. It is common to find that the parts of the organisation dismantled by accident are those that are taken for granted. Like many taken for granted relationships they are often crucial to our well being. In social services organisations, for example, we have come across several departments needing to organise new duty systems because the old ones were unintentionally taken apart when staff were relocated as part of major restructuring. In the health service we find professionals continually need to reassert the values of the relationship between staff and patients as they are unintentionally displaced by new technological procedures and equipment.

Beware of those who respond to an initiative by pointing out that the innovation has been tried before and doesn't work. Ask does the evidence suggest failure or inoculation? Did the idea work but managers fail to establish it as mainstream practice? Was the practice an accidental victim of other changes? It is common for experienced managers to have a sense of deja vu but it is good to resurrect past solutions when they are still relevant to contemporary problems.

To find the best solutions to present and future problems we need to:

- identify and sustain what works now;
- review what worked in the past;
- invent and adopt better forms of practice, service delivery and products;
- understand as many consequences of our actions as possible;
- innovate in our approaches to management to:
  - ➤ sustain effective problem solving, and
  - ➤ match management behaviour to the nature of the innovations introduced.

We cannot afford to adopt innovations just because they are the latest idea and meet all the criteria that make them easily adopted. They have to be good solutions to the problems we need to solve without causing more harm than good.

The challenge to all change agents is that they have to be prepared to confront the status quo. One consolation is that they may see themselves at the cutting edge of progress. The next generation of change agents may have to be prepared to be unfashionable as well.

REFERENCES

A full bibliography of source material can be found in the companion volume *Managing Change Through Innovation*.

Angle, H.L. and Van De Ven, A.H. (1989) Suggestions for managing the innovation journey. In Van De Ven, A.H., Angle, H.L. and Poole, M.S. (eds) Research on the Management of Innovation: The Minnesota Studies. Grand Rapids: Ballinger/Harper and Row for the University of Minnesota.

Argyris, C. (1982) Reasoning, Learning and Action: Individual and Organisational. San Francisco: Jossey Bass.

Beckhard, R. and Pritchard, W. (1992) Changing the Essence: The Art of Leading Fundamental Change in Organisations. San Francisco: Jossey Bass.

Brown, J. with Wardle, M. (1996) Chance Favours the Prepared Mind. London: HMSO.

Dommoney, L., Smale, G. and Warwick, J. (1989) Shared Care: Towards Developing Partnerships Between Health and Social Services Staff and the People They Serve. Final Report - HEA feasibility study. London: National Institute for Social Work.

Galbraith, J.K. (1991) The Guardian. November 20th.

Handy, C. (1981) Understanding Organisations. London: Penguin.

Kanter, R. Moss- (1989) When Giants Learn to Dance: Mastering the Challenges of Strategy, Management and Careers in the 1990s. New York: Simon and Schuster.

Marris, P. (1974) Loss and Change. London: Routledge and Kegan Paul.

Mosteller, F. (1981) Innovation and evaluation. Science 211, 881-886.

Newburn, T. (1993) Making a Difference? Social Work After Hillsborough. London: National Institute for Social Work.

Peters, T.J. and Waterman, R.H. (1982) In Search of Excellence: Lessons from America's Best Run Companies. New York: Harper and Row.

Rogers, E.M. (1983) The Diffusion of Innovations, New York: The Free Press.

Rogers, E.M. (1995) Diffusion of Innovation: Fourth Edition, New York: The Free Press.

Rogers, E.M. and Kincaid, D.L. (1981) Communication Networks: Toward a New Paradigm for Research. New York: The Free Press/Macmillan Publishing Company.

Schaffer, R.H. and Thompson, H.A. (1992) Sucessful change programs begin with results. Harvard Business Review, January-February.

Smale, G.G. with Tuson, G. (1992) Managing Change Through Innovation: Towards a Model for Developing and Reforming Social Work Practice and Social Service Delivery. Working Edition published by NISW, London.

Smale, G.G. (1996) Managing Change Through Innovation. HMSO, London.

Stocking, B. (1985) Initiative and Inertia: Case Studies in the N.H.S. London: Nuffield Provincial Hospital Trust.

Van De Ven, A.H., Angle, H.L. and Poole, M.S. (eds) (1989) Research on the Management of Innovation: The Minnesota Studies. Grand Rapids: Ballinger/ Harper and Row for the University of Minnesota.

Watzlawick, P., Weakland, J.H. and Fisch, R. (1974) Change: Principles of Problem Formulation and Resolution. New York, Norton.